To Alice   Jan 99.

Love from Granny

x x

A LASS FROM THE LANES

The story of a girl born in one of Lerwick's lanes

*"Her prentice hand she tried on man
And then she made the lasses O"* — Robbie Burns

James W. Irvine

A. Irvine Printing
Lerwick

First published by A. Irvine Printing 1998

ISBN 0 9522638 6 6

By the same author:
Footprints, 1980
Up-Helly-Aa, 1982
Lerwick, 1985
Dunrossness Story, 1987
The Waves are Free, 1988
The Giving Years, 1991
Men Bølgene er Jo Fri, 1993
The Years Between, 1994
Through Storm to Calm, 1995
An Island Miscellany, 1996
The Bold and The Free, 1997

Printed and published by A. Irvine Printing
4 Midgarth Crescent, Lerwick, Shetland, ZE1 0BH

Foreword

Inga Johnson, who is the central character in this story, is fictional, but the reader will find real people appearing here and there. I have frequently drawn on actual experiences in telling Inga's story

James W. Irvine

Lerwick
October 1998

Prologue

It was half-past six on a fine June morning when Alex Johnson emerged from the house where he lived in the Sooth Kirk Closs in Lerwick. Already the sun was a blinding blaze at the back of Bressay, and the vivid blue of the cloudless sky gave every indication of another lovely, Shetland summer day to come. He turned up the lane to commence his walk to his place of work - Freefield. It was the year 1833, and Alex was employed as a carpenter in the boat-building section of Hay and Ogilvy's great business at Freefield, where the dock which had been constructed was already frequently referred to as Hay's Dock. In the boatyard they had almost completed the sixern on which they were currently working, and they knew that the next job was to be a much bigger vessel. The prospect excited Alex - it would be a new challenge to them all, and, more importantly, it meant a continuation of work - and wages - for the large number of men who worked at Freefield.

As he climbed the Closs, he was more or less oblivious to his surroundings. He hardly registered the houses on both sides at the foot of the lane. They were all very much of a sameness anyway - four small windows and a door, and little visible means of ventilation. He knew there was an awful lot of people living in these houses, but he probably would have been a little surprised if he had been told that one house actually contained thirty-eight souls. His own 'house', like most other families' 'houses', was one room. In it lived his wife, her mother, little three-year old Maria and himself. That was almost luxury - only four people with a whole room to themselves! Of course, they had no running water, no toilet facilities, no proper means of cooking, and only one bed - a pretty narrow one at that. He and his wife Lizzie slept in that, mother-in-law Leebie and little Maria on the floor.

On his right, standing between his own Closs and the Nort Kirk Closs, was the Auld Kirk. It was the 'Auld' Kirk because, four years earlier, the new kirk had been completed - with room, it was said, for nine hundred and fifty-three people! Now a company had taken over the old building and had had it completely renovated under the new name of 'Subscription Rooms'. All sorts of organisations now made use of it, and it even served as the town's lock-up. Though the Masons were one of the bodies using it, it would be nearly forty years before they acquired the building for themselves. Also on his right as he walked, behind the wall of the old kirkyard, two dogs were fighting over something - probably sheep entrails or other refuse which had been dumped in over the wall. He had climbed up and looked in over a few days ago, and could hardly believe the incredible squalor of the old burial place, with trash and filth of every description littering the graves and the flattened headstones.

So accustomed was he to the little burn running down the lane that he hardly even tried to keep his feet out of it, though he well knew that most of it was urine. So what? he might have said. It has to go somewhere, and in the end it reaches the sea. As he passed the midden of human excrement a little farther up the lane, he was as usual nauseated by the stench, but he had become inured to it - and there were many similar middens throughout the town. It was all part and parcel of the town scene.

Turning west at the top of the Closs, he saw two men with a wheelbarrow turning up Bullet Loan past the Big Kirk. They had a young teenage boy in the barrow, and Alex realised they were taking him to the so-called isolation hospital at the Knab. A wheelbarrow was the nearest to an ambulance the town had yet aspired to. Every now and again there were rumours and reports of outbreaks of smallpox, or undefined 'malignant fevers', but so far Alex's family had not been stricken.

As he turned the next corner and proceeded north he came to the top of Swallow Lane and Gilbert Tait's Closs, where the road split, one branch going north to join in with Whisky Lane, the other veering left and continuing more or less to Freefield, this track basking in the high-sounding title of Wellington Road, soon to be elevated to the even more distinctive title of High Street. Now one or two of his mates were beginning to join him as he walked down Wellington Road, but their conversation was mostly monosyllabic at this early hour of the morning. On arrival at Freefield they merged with the bustle of assembling coopers, gutters, boat-builders, carpenters, smiths, masons and all the other workers who together were the life-blood of this throbbing, thriving enterprise.

This morning Alex found that his mind was not one hundred per cent on his work. His wife Lizzie was heavily pregnant, and before he left home she had begun to have pains. He felt sure that she would be in labour very shortly, and he would have liked to stay within reach. He would never have dreamed of being present at the birth - that was women's' work - but he would have liked to have been near enough to keep in touch with what was going on. "Doo's no ta worry, Alex," Lizzie had assured him. "Ah'll be ower weel. Hit's no as if hit wis da first een. By da time doo comes haem da nicht doo'll be a Dad fur da second time." All very fine, thought Alex, but what if something goes wrong? What if I were to lose Lizzie?

In their room Lizzie knew that her time had come. Down the lane lived Baabie Inkster, her good friend. Baabie had had no training, but everyone recognised her as being as good as any trained nurse or mid-wife. Lizzie's mother Leebie would go down and get her when the birth was more imminent. The idea of trying to call in a doctor or nurse was something Lizzie didn't even consider - that wasn't for 'ordinary folk'. As the morning progressed little Maria was taken to another neighbour's and Lizzie went to bed. They were all right for water. Though most of the wells in the town were more or less dry as a result of the fine weather, there was still some water in the Baker's Well, and Leebie had been over there on the previous day. She had stood for over an hour in the queue before she got her pail filled. As always, when she came back, she was full of news. As she remarked, while recounting some of the choice items she had heard, "Hit's no ta say whit you'll hear whin you're staandin in da queue fur a grain o' watter in da Baker's Closs." Had any of them paused to think they would have probably realised how valuable the water queues were for the dissemination of news, though much of what was said needed a pinch of salt, and much more could only be called slanderous.

Towards mid-day Lizzie felt the time had come to summon Baabie. She came forthwith, a cheerful, fresh-faced woman in her mid-forties. She had a look at Lizzie, pronounced everything in order, and forecast that it would probably need another hour. Lizzie was fortunate in that she was a natural child-bearer, and the birth was accomplished without much difficulty, and a minimum of pain and distress. And the result - a lovely little boy whom Baabie estimated at about eight pounds.

"Whit ir you gaain ta caa him, Lizzie?" she enquired.
"We wir tinkin if hit wis anidder lass we wid caa her Babsie, bit if hit wis a boy we wid name him John. So, my peerie ting doo's wir John." Peerie John wasn't interested - he was too busy getting stuck into his first feed. Soon he was ensconced in the little cradle, and was immediately sound asleep. Leebie fetched Maria from her temporary exile, and she inspected her new brother with great interest. She would have been all in favour of having him removed from the cradle so that she could play with him, but that was forbidden. Childbirth was still seen as a very natural function, certainly not calling for any long sojourn in bed. Lizzie was very much part of that school of thought, and to her it was perfectly natural that she should be up and preparing food for Alex when he came home at six o' clock. There was no mistaking his delight at becoming the father of a son, and he engaged in a rare public demonstration of affection by taking his wife in his arms and kissing her soundly.
"I winder whit da nixt een'll be, Lizzie - a lass or a boy?"
"Doo'll laekly no tink twa is enoff, Alex?"
"Na, lass, we'll shurly hae mair dan dat. Mebbe anidder twa or tree - whit tinks doo?"
"Yea - weel - mebbe, we'll see. Bit lat's laeve hit fur a day or twa!"

It was very nearly the longest day of the year, and there was hardly any darkness, so there was no need to light the kollie lamp - not that it gave much light anyway. They had used quite a lot of water that day because of the birth, so Leebie set out again to the Baker's Well. They knew she would be away for over an hour. Peerie John slept soundly in his cradle, and soon Maria was bedded down as well on the floor. For once Alex just sat still, puffing away at his clay pipe and hardly ever taking his eyes off his new son. Lizzie couldn't sit doing nothing, and soon the wires were busily clicking. How often, she recalled, had her mother adjured her when she was a young girl, "Lass, takk dy sock!" Lizzie was a beautiful knitter, and fine shawls were her speciality, though she also knitted all the garments her family required. She took the shawls to one of the merchants on 'da Street'. She didn't receive any money, of course - the Truck System was at its height - so she had to be satisfied with the goods she got in lieu. It was a considerable help with the living expenses, for prices in the shops were scandalous. As soon as there were a few ships in the harbour needing supplies the prices shot up. Just last week she had paid sixpence for a pound of beef!

Alex and Lizzie could both write a little, which was more than most of their contemporaries could, and, though they had no formal teaching, both could read a little, though the only book in their one-room home was an elderly Bible. Neither of them considered education a necessity for folk 'laek wis'. "Foo can readin an writin help da laek o' wis?" Alex was wont to say. But Lizzie kept her thoughts to herself. Maybe it wouldn't matter for Maria, but if it were possible to arrange it by some means or other, peerie John would be taught both to read and to write. "Some day hit'll mebbe be ta his advantage", she mused. The new addition brought much added happiness to the Johnson family in their room in da Sooth Kirk Closs. Alex went daily to his work at Freefield, and weekly he brought home his wage, so they were never short of food and could always pay the rent.

The two children grew and thrived, and so did the brother and sister who had followed them - and a fifth was on the way. Then, in 1842, Hay and Ogilvy went bankrupt. It was a tremendous blow to the whole town. Suddenly many men were without work - and without wages. Many families were immediately in dire straits, and Alex Johnson's was one of these. The future for young John looked black indeed. Now the knitting wires took on a new importance - what they produced was virtually the only income the family had. Most Shetland girls could knit by the time they were six or seven, and Maria, who was now twelve, did her bit in no small way, turning out pair after pair of mittens. While life had been set fair with Alex in steady employment at Freefield, Lizzie had managed to find the small fees required to enrol both John and Maria part-time at the Parochial School. They were both able to read and write after a fashion, but all that had to be put aside. Almost before she knew it, Lizzie was subjecting Maria to the same refrain she had heard from her mother when she was a girl, "Lass takk dy sock". But now their 'socks' were all that stood between them and starvation.

Chapter One

A Young Man at War

In 1914, when the First World War broke out, Andrew Johnson was twenty-three years of age. As his father, grandfather and great-grandfather had done before him, he lived in the room in the house in Church Lane. Overcrowding in the town was at its worst, for the population had risen to five and a half thousand. House-building had not kept pace, and many buildings were now in a sorry state, many of them classed as unfit for human habitation, though people had no option but to continue living in them. It had been a while before Andrew began to worry much about living conditions. He had always had plenty of friends of his own age, and they had never been short of a ploy to fill the idle hours. Had he been asked he would have said that, after all, things were quite a bit better than they used to be. Piped water had come to the town from the Sandy Loch in 1871. It wasn't in the houses yet, of course - except in the New Town - but they had a tap in the lane, no more standing in a queue at the Baker's Well. And the stinking middens had gone - now there were outside, flush lavatories here and there through the lanes. The old kollies had gone - gas had come, providing a minimum of street lighting in 1858, but since then the houses had gradually acquired gas lights.

But, Andrew had thought wryly, as he lay on his palliasse one night waiting for sleep to come, the thing that's made the biggest difference to my life compared to my Dad's is education and the coming of the new schools. He well remembered the reluctance with which he had directed his steps to the new infant school which had been built in 1876 in what was to become Albany Street - and later St Olaf Street - and then, in 1901, had come the edict that everyone had to stay at school until the age of fourteen. They had thought that was a bad blow. In the following year the great new Central School had been opened. His final years of school had been spent there, and, in retrospect, it hadn't been too bad. A bit like the army, he supposed, with all the strict discipline. But he had learned to read, and he had discovered just how much he liked reading books. And even though they didn't get much in the way of music, he had discovered that he loved music. Then he had learned to write and to count and all the other bits and pieces - and perhaps more importantly in view of the unknown which lay ahead of him, he had learned to speak English - though he hated it.

In those days there were no Youth Clubs, and, though the North Star Cinema had opened in 1913, it was still not a place much frequented by penurious young people. But there was always the harbour. And what a place it was at the height of the herring fishing, especially in the days at the turn of the century when the boats were all under sail - hundreds of them filling Bressay Sound. In Andrew's younger days they had all landed their catches at Freefield, but when Alexandra Wharf was constructed in 1906 all catches were auctioned there, and the building of the Fish Market in 1907 made that the beating heart of the little town during the summer months.

And what a place Commercial Street was on a Saturday night. Andrew and his friends couldn't resist its fascinations. The fishing fleet lay tied up for the weekend, and the boys well knew the significance of their registration letters - the PD, FR, INS, BCK, BF, etc. all denoting boats from the Scottish north-east ports and the Moray Firth towns, while YH and LT were the English boats from Yarmouth and Lowestoft. Their crews all came ashore on a Saturday night, and they were nearly always joined by baggy-trousered Dutchmen off their fishing boms, plus frequently some Norwegian, Danish or Swedish fishermen. Then there were the gutter girls from their huts on the curing stations, all fresh and bright in their best frocks, most of them from the north of Scotland and the Western Isles. The strong dialects of East Anglia and north-east Scotland mingled with the occasional Gaelic of the Western Isles' girls, the Dutch and Scandinavian languages and the broad Shetlandic, to form an amazing cacophony of sound. All the shops stayed open until late, and they did a roaring trade, not least in the sale of pandrops to the young Dutchmen! This cosmopolitan throng, amounting to many hundreds, wandered from one end of the Street to the other, time after time turning and retracing their steps. Those going north kept to one side, those going south to the other. Here and there musicians played, and one or two cheap-jacks extolled their wares.

The boys were part and parcel of the throng. This was Life with a capital L, and they strained to be part of it, savouring every moment. Parents didn't worry if they were out late, for this was an orderly gathering. There were no riots, there were no fights. Lerwick's police force was considered adequate to deal with the added presence of several thousands of assorted incomers - it consisted of the police chief and one constable!

One day in an idle moment Andrew and his pals discussed what they would do when the glorious day arrived on which they could leave school. It was taken for granted they would all leave school at the earliest moment after they reached the age of fourteen. None of them had any thought of going on for further education. That still wasn't a viable option for 'da laeks o' wis'. In any case they had to start earning just as soon as possible.

"I ken whit Ah'm gaun ta do," declared Alex. "Me fedder's spokken ta da skipper o' *da Brighter Morn*, an' he's promised ta takk me fur bush-boy/cook as shun as I laeve skul." There was some criticism of his statement.

"Whit does doo ken aboot da herrin an' gaun ta sea? Doo's nivir been aff in dee life!" But Alex was impervious to criticism - his future was mapped out.

" I wid laek ta makk barrels," stated Jeemsy. "Ah'm watched da coopers wirkin ever sae aft, an' Ah'm gaun ta try an git Smith an Schultze ta takk me on. John Adamson wirks dere an' he's promised ta pit in a wird fur me."

" I ken whaur Ah'm gaun," declared Robbie. "R an' C hiv promised ta takk me on as a message-boy, an' dan later Ah'll git da shance ta staund ahint da coonter."

"Whit aboot dee, Andrew?" asked one of the boys.

"I dunna ken, bit I wid laek ta laern ta be a carpenter. Dat's whit me fedder an' me grandfedder an' even me great-grandfedder aa did."

"I ken whaur Ah'm gaun ta try fur a job," revealed Willie. "Hit's at Ganson's. Da man dere lats me help wi feeding da horses, an he says whin Ah'm auld enoff I kin laern to drive een o' da gigs."

So, without much in the way of careers' advice, the boys planned their way of life. But conversation abruptly came to an end as the huge grey bows of a very large ship came into view in the south harbour. "Hit's a battleship," shouted Robbie, and the boys were off at a run to get a better view of the massive Dreadnought.

The boys all duly reached the school leaving-age of fourteen, and their lives developed more or less as they had planned. The Johnson men had all had good hands, and Andrew was no exception. Perhaps he owed a little to his father's good offices, but he was taken on at Hay's, and in due course became a fully fledged carpenter - and a really good one. Like most young men of his age who had a job, life didn't present him with too many worries. They had to make their own entertainment, but there were occasional dances and concerts, and there was always Up-Helly-Aa. For Andrew the annual festival was something special. Thanks to his skill as a carpenter, and the fact that he worked at Freefield, he became one of the Docks' Boys who each year provided a magnificent ship model to be part of the Festival. So impressive were their contributions that, in 1912, they were asked to take over the building of the galley. Their skill produced the best galley that had been seen so far, and henceforth they were to be the recognised galley builders. Every year the Festival was becoming more impressive, with halls open for the entertainment of the guizers.

Andrew was quite capable of enjoying the company of the opposite sex, and, apart from one or two minor liaisons, he had had a bit of a fling with a lass from Harris who was up for the fishing season. But it wasn't serious, and no thought of marriage had ever entered his head. He had watched Robby and Tammy both getting married - in some haste be it said - when they were little more than twenty, and he had indeed been best man to Robbie. He had no intention of following suit. "Dere's nae hurry fur yon," he told himself. Now and again his mother would give him a dig. "Will nane o' da lasses hae onything ta dö wi dee?" she would prod. "Na, mom, dey winna look at me," he would answer her solemnly. Whereupon he would depart blithely for a night out with the boys.

Barbara Henderson was a dark-haired, blue-eyed lass of twenty, who had come to the town with her mother when her father, a sixern man, was lost at sea. They belonged to Papa Stour, but a widowed mother had little chance of making a living there. They had hoped they might stand a better chance in the town. In their case their hopes were justified, for mother Kirsty got work 'in-service' in one of the big houses in King Harald Street. They were also lucky enough to find a room in Reform Lane, and Barbara, on leaving school, was also taken 'into service' in the same house as her mother. The families with money - mostly 'herring' money - who had built the fine new houses in the New Town quickly acquired the ability to live in the style of the rich, and that, of course, involved having servants. Before the New Town was opened up the men with money had lived cheek by jowl with the ordinary folk in the lanes, under the same atrocious conditions, but now they were getting out, and the division between the 'haves' and the 'have-nots' became increasingly more pronounced.

Andrew and Barbara were well aware of the electricity between them, but their relationship continued for some time with neither making anything in the way of a definite declaration. As far as Andrew was concerned, he was in no doubt that he was in love with Barbara. None of the other girls with whom he had dallied had been so nice to cuddle, none so nice to kiss - and none of them had made him impatient for the next meeting. But he was ambitious enough to feel that he would like something better than a room in a Lerwick lane for the girl he married. Barbara was sure enough about her feelings, too, but as much as she would have liked to give him a push, it was up to Andrew to make the first move.

Into this unresolved situation came the First World War. Andrew watched the RNR boys going, he listened to the raucous bellows of the NCOs training the Terriers in the Fort, and he felt increasingly that he, too, must do his bit. Finally he could stand it no longer and joined up, obeying Kitchener's pointing finger on the poster, telling him 'Your country Needs You.' He was posted immediately to the Seaforths. Before he went off he belatedly told Barbara that he loved her.

"Why did doo wait till doo wis gaun awa afore doo telled me?" she demanded. "Did doo hae nae idea dat Ah'm loved dee fur monts?" Andrew was indeed sorry by this time that he had not made his declaration earlier - what a lot of time they had wasted. "Ah'll mak it up ta dee," he assured her. "Dis war'll no lest lang an dan Ah'll be hame again an we kin git married." In the few days left they spent as much time as they could in each other's company, but all too soon it was down to the pier and on board the steamer. As he held her close at the foot of the gangway Barbara could no longer restrain the tears. Will I ever see him again?, she wondered. She knew only too well from the reports coming from France just how heavy were the casualties Britain was suffering. As he mounted the gang-plank and then stood waving to Barbara till the pier disappeared from view, Andrew's heart was the heaviest it had been in his young life. Just what lies ahead he wondered.

After what seemed a remarkably short period of training, Andrew found himself on a trooper crossing the Channel, and within a few days, he was in the trenches. He had seen in the papers that journalists had dubbed the conflict 'trench warfare', but nothing he had read had prepared him for the horror, the degradation, the danger and the filth which made up the so-called 'trench warfare'. There could be nothing nearer hell on earth. Living in the trenches often waterlogged, always infested with rats, with lice rampant on their bodies and never even a hot meal - that wasn't living - at best it was existing. Add to that frequent bombardments by the heavy German guns, with deadly shrapnel tearing into human bodies, with ears deafened by the thunderous blasts, it was no wonder that after a time they moved like bemused automatons. Every now and again there was an attack on the German lines. Dulled with a dollop of rum, on the blast of a whistle they would climb over the parapet, and, carrying their rifles with bayonets fixed, they would set off at a shambling trot across the cratered, slimy surface which was No Man's Land, towards the German trenches perhaps a hundred yards away. British artillery always pasted the enemy front trenches immediately before an attack, but from the moment they appeared over the parapet the enemy machine-guns would open up, and men would begin to fall almost as soon as they left their trenches. It was not surprising that the men soon lost confidence in the effectiveness of the British bombardments of the enemy trenches. Usually in these attacks only a handful of men actually reached the German barbed wire. More often than not the wounded lay where they dropped until the stretcher bearers could get to them when darkness fell. And yet it was in such situations that man's love for his fellow man was sometimes seen at its best, for frequently heroic efforts were made by his pals to rescue a man lying wounded in No Man's Land. How infrequently were medals handed out for such acts - it was more often for the killing of the enemy - preferably in large numbers - that medals were awarded.

In 1916 a piece of shrapnel got Andrew in the leg - a wound serious enough to take him to Blighty. He came home on sick leave, to be received by Barbara's open arms, but this was not the Andrew she had known. He was so much quieter - in fact there were periods when he didn't speak at all, and sometimes he simply sat staring into space. Barbara understood something of what he had been through and didn't push him - just offered her love. It didn't seem long till he was fit again, and off he went, still cocooned in his own secret world. Barbara worried ceaselessly about the state he was in. Most of all she feared for his mind.

Back in the trenches Andrew found not a single one of his old pals remaining. In their place were young conscripts with a minimum of training, still wet behind the ears and looking to old-stager Sergeant Johnson for help and guidance. Still the criminals called generals were sending these boys to be massacred in the abattoirs of the Western Front. More and more nerves were breaking, causing men to turn in the midst of an attack and try to regain their own trenches. Such men received a summary court-martial and were shot for cowardice or desertion. Andrew saw it all as if from a distance. "When will I break? " he wondered. Then, in late 1917, a German bullet found its mark in his side during another fruitless attack, and he slid unconscious into a slimy shell-hole where, with a corpse from a previous raid for company, he lay half-submerged all day until found by the stretcher-bearers after darkness fell. Somehow he survived, but this time his hospital treatment continued for many weeks, until he found himself once more at home on convalescent leave. Strangely, Barbara found him more communicative this time, and it seemed as if he had come out of his own secret little world. Could it be, she wondered, that his mind had simply reached the point where nothing, no matter how terrible, could affect him any more.

"Dö's doo ken, Barbara, Ah'm da only een left oot o' da company it I guid across ta France wi? Da Germans needna try ony mair. Dey kinna kill me!"

"Oh, I hoop dat's true Aandrew. Doo doesna ken just foo muckle I want dee ta cum back ta me."

With a cheerfulness which she knew was unreal, he reached the end of his sick leave and went back again. Incredibly, he was once more classified A1 and sent back to the trenches. Senior NCOs with the experience Andrew had were hard to come by, and he was just the sort of man the army desperately needed, either to lead on to victory or meet a last desperate push by the enemy. In 1918 it both happened. The enemy push came first and faltered. The Allied push followed, now bolstered by the arrival of American troops. When the Armistice came in November, 1918, the Allies were adjudged the victors. But only just. Andrew survived and returned home, demobbed, early in 1919.

Chapter Two

Lerwick Family Life In The Twenties

The young man who had gone to war in 1914 never returned, but gradually, thanks in no small measure to Barbara's love and understanding, his memories of the horrors which had been the First World War began to dim, and something like the old Andrew began to function again. But everything had changed - so many of his old friends had gone, never to return. Shetland had suffered terribly in relation to her population. To begin with in the post-war days there was work, and Andrew benefited with the rest. Then the Town Council, in 1920, decided to build 120 new houses. These would be followed by many more in the years that stretched ahead, but it was an ambitious first step by a small Council to meet what was a crying need. Andrew had no trouble being taken on as a carpenter to work on this new scheme, which guaranteed work for several years.

Since his return from the war Barbara had become even more dear to him, and clearly she felt the same way about Andrew. But though they had discussed marriage, he was always the one to drag his feet. What had he got to offer a new wife? At best, a room in a lane. He looked with longing at the impressive new houses which had been built in the New Town, and he looked closely at how the Council houses in the brand new Knab Road and Breiwick Road areas would appear when they were completed, and he thought - if only! But he had to accept that there were many families living in terrible conditions who would take precedence over Barbara and himself when the new houses were being let.

Then, quite suddenly, he got the chance of a room in Chapel House, Mounthooly Street. It was a big room on the ground floor - big enough for two beds. He closed the deal immediately, and that same day he and Barbara decided to get married. The ceremony was duly performed late in 1921, and the young couple, accompanied by ma-in-law Kirsty, took up residence immediately. Had you asked them where they were going for their honeymoon, they would have laughed. The idea of a honeymoon had not at that time become a realisable dream for most young newly-weds. But it was a good room - almost luxury, as Barbara said, and certainly much better than the rooms they had lived in in Church Lane and Reform Lane.

Apart from living together, nothing much else changed. Barbara and Kirsty continued 'in service'. Andrew kept on his job on the new housing scheme. 1922 passed, and in 1923 the great new scheme was completed - 120 houses of which the town could be justly proud. As Andrew had surmised, they didn't qualify for tenancy of one of them, but he found another job when the scheme was finished. By then Kirsty had almost given up hope of ever being a granny, but in 1924 the first-born arrived - a son. Both parents - not to mention granny - were over the moon about the boy, as well they might be for John was a sturdy, bonny boy. Again the years passed without any addition, but in 1927 number two arrived. This time it was a girl - a little, dark-haired, blue eyed mite, and if Andrew's boy had delighted him, his girl was even more special. From the first moment he laid eyes on her, little Inga wound him round her tiny little finger. As Andrew proudly told Barbara one night, as she stretched to rock the cradle which stood beside the bed, when Inga whimpered gently in her sleep, "We raelly ir a faimly noo, Barbara!"

As the days passed tiny Inga grew and gurgled, until one day she 'slippit da hadd', and made an uncertain voyage right across the room. She repeated this feat after Dad came home from work, and it was hard to say which was the prouder - Dad or Inga. It seemed no time at all till she was big enough to be let out in the lane to play under the watchful eye of big brother John. Soon they left their Chapel House to flit across the Closs to another house where they had two rooms - a big one on the ground floor and a smaller bedroom up a narrow stair. Here they had their own front door. This was a distinct improvement on Chapel House where there had been five different tenants using the same front door.

In the big downstairs room the stove stood opposite the door, and there was a table in front of the window. A large bed stood in the corner, and here Dad, Mom and Inga slept. John slept on the floor, and granny Kirsty's bed was in the small room upstairs. A curtained recess provided sanitary privacy when required, for none of these houses, so far, had had piped water installed. This was obtained from a tap in the Closs. Down the Closs, and round the corner in Navy Lane were two flush toilets which served the needs of the neighbouring tenants in both Baker's Closs (Mounthooly Street was still too much of a mouthful) and Navy Lane. Sanitary waste from the houses was also disposed of here.

Most of the houses now had gas lighting, and one night John awoke coughing, his coughing rousing his parents and little Inga. Andrew soon discovered the cause of the coughing to be gas, and he quickly evacuated his family and the woman next door into the Closs, until the source of the leak could be established.

Soon Inga was big anough to play with the other children in the Closs without the constant supervision of mother or big brother John. It was a relatively safe playground, for it was rare to see a car in the lane, and the most dangerous vehicle as far as the children were concerned was the occasional bicycle. There was a small drying green on the opposite side of the lane which served most of the neighbours, and on this side, too, was a fine modern house occupied by John Linklater (of R & C's) and his wife. This house even had a flush toilet. Inga recalled some of the children who went up and down the Closs almost daily. The two youngest boys from a family of ten children who lived in Ronald Street were a familiar sight, though years older than she. Even as a little girl she realised that they were lively boys, and she could recall a trick they played more than once. Several of the houses in the lane had their doors side by side, and the two lads would go to the drying green, take the clothes' line and use it to tie together the handles of the two side by side doors. Having done so, they would knock on the doors, then scamper quickly to hiding. In response to the boys' knocking it was clear that someone in each house would come to the doors and attempt to open them. To no avail. After some fruitless endeavour there would be a pause before a knife blade could be seen appearing through the crack of a slightly opened door, and the imprisoning rope would be cut. Sadly the hunt for the culprits was always non-productive - they had disappeared.

By the time Inga was four Dad was taking her to church with him on a Sunday. Dad was an excellent singer, and Inga discovered very early in life that she, too, loved singing. Soon she was attending church for the morning service, then off to Sunday School, then finally to the evening service with Dad. The mornings were always to the big kirk, but the evenings were sometimes Congregational, sometimes Baptist. At the age of four she found herself the youngest child at the Sunday School Christmas party. Because she was the youngest she was given the doll off the beautifully decorated Christmas tree. She was overwhelmed - the doll was big and beautiful - she had never had anything so wonderful. Then one of the bigger boys snatched it from her and dropped it. It broke. Thus early did tragedy strike a very small girl.

When she was five she sang a solo in the Big Kirk. She could never recall the circumstances that led to this, but she never forgot standing, a tiny morsel, in front of the choir, pouring out 'Away in a Manger'. When she was a little older Bella Hunter and Joey Robertson trained them every year for the Sunday School Nativity Musical - everybody who could sing, that was. She always remembered that, when she was an angel, the tinsel decoration round her head itched and made her want to scratch. At home on a Sunday the rules were strict. No activity which would in any way break the sanctity of the Sabbath. No singing of anything except hymns.

She learned to knit at the age of five. Collecting scraps of yarn from her mother and her aunts, she made a scarf for her doll. The yarn looked a bit dirty and she washed the scarf when completed, only to find that the imagined dirt was in fact different coloured yarn, so that her first effort had something of Fair Isle in it!

Dad had a good enough job as jobs went in those days, but it was a special week indeed when his earnings amounted to £2. That didn't run to much in the way of luxuries. When food for a week had been bought, the rent paid, and something put by for clothes, there was never anything left. If she was lucky, and there was a spare penny on a Saturday night, then it was down to Peter Leisk's shop to spend it. It was surprising how much sweetness a penny could buy. Often there were some bruised apples or pears, and, with the bad bits cut off, these could be bought for a ha'penny. Food was never over-plentiful, but she couldn't remember ever being hungry. One thing was for sure - no one ever heard her or John saying, "Mom, I dunna laek dis - Ah'm no gaun ta aet it," when a meal was set on the table. They had soup frequently, and quite a bit of beef on which the soup was made. Of course fish was a standby - fish were still relatively cheap, and sometimes Dad would come with a 'fry' given to him by a friend on one of the fishing boats. Mom still had relations in Papa, and every year at least one lamb arrived in the Closs for the Johnsons. When that happened Mom always made puddings, and all of them enjoyed that delicacy. Aunt Maggie from Papa had married a Sandness man with a croft, and tatties arrived from there every now and again. But if she had to choose Inga would have said, "My favourite is sassermaet." So, although life in Da Baker's Closs in the twenties and early thirties was no bed of roses, Inga was reasonably well fed, and, thanks to her mother's skill on her sewing machine, she never had to go inadequately clad.

As Inga and her little friends skipped and played in the Closs, she got to know all the familes who lived in the neighbouring houses. There were the Knights, the Mustards, the Duncans, the Johnstones, the Leslies, the Leiths - and there was Mr

Hyslop's market garden. There was Bruce Laurenson's dental surgery, Frank Williamson's shop, and there was the 'Shetland News', to which came daily two respected gentlemen, Mr Mortimer Manson and Mr Bob Inkster. T. J. Anderson's shop at the foot of the Closs seemed to be a shop everyone was familiar with. Often the children would go up to the top of the Closs and out on to the Hillhead to play. Between them and the top of Queen's Lane were two workshops, Duncan and Bolt and George Gair. Duncan and Bolt of course had the hearse, and in those days it was pulled by a big black horse. The big horse and the hearse, all in black, was an awesome and sombre sight for the children, and, when they were playing happily at the Hillhead, there would sometimes come the shout, "Da horse!" That shout was the warning of the coming of the horse and the hearse. On hearing the shout all play ceased, the children rushed to the roadside and there, frozen in terror, they stood like statues, without a movement, without a sound, until the apparition had passed. The fact that it was gran'dad driving the horse made the scene no less terrifying for Inga.

"Wis doo faerd, Inga?" one of her pals would ask. "Yea, I wis terrified," Inga would reply, then they would all compare notes on just how frightened they had been. Not even the brashest of the boys attempted to bluff it out and claim a lack of fear.

Chapter Three

School

There came the night when Mom said,
"Hit's skul fur dee da moarn, my bairn."
Da moarn was the first day of school after the Easter holidays,
and Inga, having reached five, was due to enrol. It was an
exciting thought, mixed with some misgivings. But two of her
pals from the Closs were also enrolling, so at least she would
know somebody.

Her mother came with her in the morning, and they waited with
the other mothers and children until all the older classes had
lined up in their twos, and had been marched into school. Inga
watched this operation with interest. "We'll be doin yon da
moarn," she thought. Then it was their turn to be taken in, to
Room 1, where all their particulars, as supplied by the Moms,
were written down, and they were officially enrolled under their
new teacher whose name, she told them, was Miss Deyell. Then
it was time for Mom to go. Taking her leave of her daughter
was as matter-of-fact as Barbara could make it.
"So, bairn, Ah'll hae ta laeve dee noo. Just be a good lass an dö
whit doo's telled." With a little cuddle for Inga she was gone,
and, though there might have been tears at the back of Inga's
eyes, she was determined not to cry. But the situation sure was

frightening for a very shy little girl - it was all so new. They were allocated to their desks, and when all were seated, and the teacher had counted them, she announced that the class numbered forty-one. Then they were told to stand, and they embarked on the first attempt at "Our Father----" chanted in unison after Miss Deyell. This would be repeated every morning during their primary school career. It was no problem to Inga, a regular church-goer from the age of four and endowed with a remarkable memory. She had learned the Lord's Prayer long ago. They were told that Miss Deyell was to be addressed as Miss - "Please Miss," "Yes, miss," and so on. And they got reading books. They were well-worn, having passed through numerous previous owners' hands, but the book was new to Inga, and she was delighted with it, for she could read some already, and when she got home from school, instead of dashing out to play, she sat with the new book, laboriously ploughing her way through the script. Mom was regaled with a lot of stories about the first day at school - and she couldn't wait for the morning to come so she could go again.

She soon became accustomed to lining up in their twos, marching into the hall/cloakroom, taking off their coats, then making their way into the classroom, again in their twos. (She was to find that the hall/cloakroom also had to serve as the P.E. hall as and when required.) On this second day writing was one of the lessons. Inga was one of the minority - she was left-handed. Mom had heard that teachers at school were compelling left-handed children to write with their right hand. Mom, a lass from Papa, whose working life had been spent largely 'in service', had a highly developed sense of the need for respect for your 'betters', and so, to do as much as she could to smooth the path for her little girl, she had succeeded in teaching Inga to write with her right hand before she went to school. So for Inga, what might have been a traumatic hurdle in her early school life was removed even before it appeared. There were only two other left-handers in her class - she was later to realise that both of them, like herself, had grandparents from Papa. The toilets and playsheds were at the far side of the playground, and, when there was a strong south-easterly wind and driving rain, you thought twice about whether your journey was really necessary and you needed 'leave out'. It wasn't long before Inga felt quite at home in school - just one of nearly two hundred who attended the Old Infant daily. She was painfully shy, but she had an excellent memory, and, though she wasn't aware of it, she was very intelligent, so the classroom held few problems and few terrors for the little girl from the Closs.

The first years passed and then it was up to the Central, Miss Deyell still with them. Here the girls and boys had their own separate playgrounds, but it was still an adventure to reach the outside toilets on a really bad day. Regimentation was even more rigorous here, but as they were once again the youngest, Inga's class lined up nearest the girls' entrance door. On the other side of school the boys from their class would be duplicating their actions. Mr Spalding was often present in the playground to supervise behaviour, and a teacher would come out when the bell rang to make sure that all classes entered in a seemly and orderly fashion.

In the Central they were very conscious that Mr Durham was their Headmaster. When they came into school he would be standing up on the balcony watching their entrance to their rooms. Stories about him being a stickler for discipline were rife in the school, and there were many accounts of the punishments he had meted out. The little newcomers from the Infant School went in a constant state of terror of incurring his wrath. To their surprise he came into their classroom one day and took them for a lesson. There was no sign of the frightening side of his character, and the class soon forgot their terror. As Inga said to her mother that night,

"Mom, Mr Durham wis in aside wis da day. He tellt wis aboot Horatio an da Bridge, an I wisna faerd fur him ava."

By the time they had had experience of Miss Deyell, Miss Nessie Garriock, Miss Dolly Harrison, and Mrs Groat as teachers, they had reached the end of their primary education. As far as Inga was concerned, she had enjoyed it. School had its ups and downs, but she reckoned that on balance the ups far outweighed the downs. There were highlights. Prize days for instance. The whole of the primary would be assembled in the hall, and up on the platform would be arranged a number of local luminaries. She always enjoyed it when Mrs A. J. Smith was among them, because she always told them a story - something she was very good at. There were always five merit prizes for each class, plus one for progress and one for attendance. When a prize-winner's name was called, he or she would march up to the podium to receive the book being handed over by one of the dignitaries on the platform. If a boy, you saluted, if a girl, you bowed. It didn't strike Inga as strange that every year she was one of the prize-winners - her innate shyness made the journey from her seat to the podium quite an ordeal - and then her first interest was to see whether the book she had received would be one she would enjoy reading.

The business of bowing by the girls and saluting by the boys had to be observed whenever a teacher was encountered outside school hours. Inga heard a story about one of the Ronald Street boys, and she didn't doubt its truth for a moment. The boy had met the Headmaster on Commercial Street and had duly saluted, sadly forgetting that he had a cigarette in his mouth at the time. That, of course, was a heinous crime, and the next morning he was duly summoned to the Headmaster's room for punishment. The sentence was six strokes of the tawse on each hand - no light penance, and Mr Spalding was in attendance to ensure that there were no hitches in the execution of the sentence. The boy held out one hand and had six severe strokes duly delivered. The order was given for the other hand to be extended. The boy had had enough. The severity of the strokes was such that, if both hands had to endure the punishment, he wouldn't be able to use either. He stated clearly "That's enoff. Nae mair." Mr Spalding was ordered to grasp the recalcitrant arm and hold out the hand. As he proceeded to do this the boy, shod in thick-soled boots with iron toe-caps, drew back a leg and delivered a powerful blow to Mr Spalding's leg just below the knee. Mr Spalding emitted a howl of agony, let go the boy's arm, and hopped on one leg. The boy said, "I telled you - nae mair!" then disappeared at a run along the balcony, down the stairs, out the door and home. Strangely the boy suffered no repercussions for this affair, which was, perhaps, significant commentary on the event.

Belting or strapping was fairly common in these days, and perhaps it was not surprising that it gave rise to not a few well-embellished stories. Inga heard one account of how a certain teacher sometimes felt called on to use the strap. It was clearly a task she did not enjoy, for she always closed her eyes as she brought her strap down. The culprit would be standing with both hands extended - she wanted to be sure she had a target big enough to prevent a miss. But culprits, in the very nature of things, are pretty fly, and her eye-closed strapping system was well-known to all the habitual miscreants. They would stand with hands extended, watching carefully for the eyes to close.

Then the hands were swiftly separated, and the strap would descend through the space between, without finding a target. Fortunately for the boys the teacher always seemed to feel that it was a case of mission accomplished, and the baddies would return to their seats none the worse. Then there was the story of the boy who fled from headmasterly punishment, went over the balcony rail, hung briefly from the bottom of the rail, then dropped what must have seemed a huge distance to the hard floor of the hall below. Amazingly he got up, no bones broken, and fled. His place in school lore was secure.

The Ronald Street boys were well known to Inga, and, because they were so much older and bigger, were something in the nature of heroes. She could remember them standing at the foot of the Closs one Saturday night, when the Street was crowded with its usual cosmopolitan throng. The boys had obviously seen the town policeman approaching among the crowd. When he was still a short distance away the boys uttered a shout to draw attention to themselves, then started to run south along the Street, dodging among the people. The policeman, affectionately known as 'Gentle Aanie', seeing them running away immediately gave chase. His philosophy was that anyone running away, especially boys, when they saw him coming, had to be guilty of something. Of course the boys were also well aware that they had the nimbleness and speed to elude him. On this occasion that proved to be the case and the mischievous minds had produced another successful prank.

Dad had gone for a walk around the golf course one day and had taken Inga with him. Looking seawards over the golf course wall they discovered that, immediately below them, were her two heroes from Ronald Street. One of them was sitting in the sea in an inflated car tyre inner tube, looking down into the sea through some sort of funnel - probably a pail - which apparently had a glass end. The other boy was diving repeatedly and reappearing on the surface with small white objects which he would hand to the brother seated in the tube. Dad and Inga finally concluded that the boys' sunken treasure trove was golf balls which had been driven into the sea by over-lusty golfers. She afterwards learned that the boys were able to sell the recovered balls for tuppence - less than 1p - but that was pretty good reward for a boy if he had a dozen or so to sell. The car tubes were clearly put to much good use, for one day she saw the boys come paddling in past the Deuk's Neb. They had come all the way from the Waari Geo.

Chapter Four

A Cooncil Hoose

As Inga progressed through the Primary, a great event in her life took place. When she and John came home from school one night, her mother's excitement was plain to see.

"Whit's wrang, Mom? Whit's happened?" they both demanded.

"Dere's naethin wrang, bairns. Tell me, whit wid you baith laek mair dan onything?" The bairns didn't even need time to think.

"A new hoose, Mom." they chorused.

"Weel, dat's whit we're gittin. A new hoose in Commercial Rodd!"

Although the house was not yet ready, Dad had found out which one it was to be, and that evening Dad, Mom and the bairns proceeded to Commercial Road just to look at the new building. The allocation of the new house probably meant more to Inga than any of the others. A sensitive lass, she mixed with the children of well-to-do families in her class at school. The girls from the fine new houses in the New Town had their own bedrooms, and, above all, baths and flush toilets. Even those families which had been allocated one of the new houses in Knab Road or Breiwick Road were living in luxury compared with a room in a Closs. Now at last the Johnsons, too, would have the chance to live in a decent house, and she wouldn't have constantly to feel inferior to most of her classmates. The fact that one or two other families from her Closs had also now been allocated new houses made it all even more exciting.

When they came home from their visit to Commercial Road, Inga and John had a lot of questions to ask.

"Foo mony bedrooms will dere be in da new hoose?" Inga wanted to know. Mom well knew where that question was leading.

"Dere'll be tree bedrooms," she replied. "Bit afore doo aksis, doo canna hae een ta deesel yit. Doo'll hae ta share wi granny."

"Whit aboot me?" John wondered.

"Yea, doo'll hae a room an Dad and me will hae da idder een."

"Will we hae a wireless set?" came next.

"No yit," said Dad. "We hae dat mony idder things ta git fur da new hoose we canna afford a wireless yit."

"Will dere be a keetchin ta do da cookin in?" Inga wondered. Dad was of the opinion that a small room which some called a scullery would serve as a kitchen, for it had a chimney and they could take their stove from the Closs and install it at Commercial Road.

The day came in October, 1935, when they got the key to their new house. When they went and had a look round, their first impressions were of the amount of space there was in the house compared with all they had had in the Closs. There were the three bedrooms Mom had told them about. As Inga had half expected she and Granny were allocated the back room. Its window looked straight out the Nort Mooth. The adjacent back door opened directly into the kitchen, and when the wind was northerly the back room was anything but warm. But she didn't mind - now she had a half share in a room. With the stove from the Closs installed in the scullery it made an adequate kitchen. The living-room was quite big, and in it was a large range - a big, black creature which had the purpose of providing heat and cooking facilities. It had an excellent oven and it served its cooking requirements well. But the firebox was small, and the heat had to emerge into the room between six small firebars - always inadequate for heating a large room. All the bedrooms had open fireplaces. But there wasn't a single power-point anywhere in the house, so there was no electric fire, no electric kettle, no electric cooker - but there was electric light. And there was a bathroom. Inga promised herself that as soon as they had got a fire going and the water heated up she would have a bath - she couldn't wait!

Their house in reality was a ground-floor flat, and another family lived in the flat above. Insulation between the two was not very good, and at times the noise from above could be considerable. But that was a small niggle compared with the joy of having a proper, modern house to live in. By this time Inga's love of music was very strong, and she longed to have a wireless set so that they could listen to all the music programmes and the big band dance music. However, the family of one of her pals had a set, and she was often invited in to listen. She was there when Edward VIII announced his abdication in order to marry the 'woman he loved'. While there were many who thought Edward's actions overly dramatic, and maybe even indicative of a man who would have proved a light-weight king, many girls found the whole episode very romantic, and most of them felt this was indeed a real love story. Privately Inga thought Edward must be a silly ass, for she had seen a picture of Mrs Simpson and had not considered her to be the sort of raving beauty that kings might give up their throne for. She couldn't really foresee a time when some man might do something similar out of love for her!

The only thing that marred the happiness of the Johnson family in their new house was the fact that times had become hard again, and Dad was sometimes out of work. But all that was put aside in July, 1936, when a little sister arrived. Inga was now old enough to be capable of sitting with the baby on her knee, and very proud she felt when entrusted with that responsible task. Her love of singing came in handy now, and time and again she would patiently croon the baby to sleep.

It would all have been so fine - new house, new sister, happy school - what more could anyone want. But before baby sister was a year old tragedy struck. The marks which war had left on Dad finally caught up with him, and he died in March, 1937. Though Inga's early years had seen plenty of hardship, nothing remotely like this had ever happened up to now. The days following Dad's death were days she would never forget. At first she simply couldn't believe that it had happened. Then gradually she had to come to terms with the reality of the tragedy - how could this gaping void in her young life ever be filled? The tears were seldom from her eyes. But young as she was she realised that the loss must be even worse for her mother. Left with three young children to care for, the breadwinner gone, she must already be at her wit's end as to how they were going to manage. Even so, Barbara found time to cuddle and console the bairns, while at the same time busying herself with dyeing all their clothes black. Ever afterwards Inga would associate black clothes with grief, and she never wore black things again. Well-meaning people came to visit, condole, and have a last look at Dad where he lay so peacefully in the open coffin. In a way the day of the funeral was a relief, for the open coffin was lidded and carried out to the hearse. In these days women simply did not go to funerals, but brother John had to face the ordeal.

The days that followed were hard to bear, with the grief remaining raw and wrenching. But the realities of the situation, with mere existence a pressing problem, also had to be faced. John and Inga were both old enough to realise that they were in real trouble. With Dad no longer there to bring in a wage, and to provide answers to all life's problems, big and small, everything devolved on Mom. John was a big boy for his age, just entered on his secondary course at the school, and he manfully assured his mother that he would look after her. Inga, too, offered reassurance, and promised all the help she could give. In reality knitting was the only practical way she could help, and now she devoted every spare moment to her 'wires', and, young though she was, was soon producing impressive numbers of Fair Isle gloves. Though her mother would automatically adjure her, "Bairn, takk dy sock," she didn't have to be told. There was the widow's pension, but it was a pittance. No matter how hard they worked, the combined output of Mom and Inga's wires were far from enough to keep the wolf from the door. Mom did alterations to clothes on her sewing machine for lots of folk, but it was still not enough. There was one asset - they had three bedrooms. A bed was set up for Mom and little sister in the living room, and one bedroom was freed for a lodger or lodgers. For years, almost without a break, there were lodgers, and the income from that added to the other bits and pieces, gave the family enough to pay their way. Once again there were never many pennies to spare, but they managed. But it took a long time for the sadness engendered by Dad's death to wane and for life to return to something like normal.

Chapter Five

Country Visits

Mom's sister Lizzie had married a Sandness man with a croft, and from the age of four Inga used to go out to Sandness every summer to spend several weeks with her aunt and uncle. They had a son and daughter, both older than Inga. Inga loved her visits to the country. The man who drove the small Sandness bus, Lowrie Duncan, lived next door to Auntie Lizzie, and he would stop outside Jim Taylor's to pick up little Inga in Commercial Road. Her mother knew that she was in good hands when she entrusted her to Lowrie. Inga loved the bus journeys out to Sandness - for her they never lasted long enough. Her favourite parts were going through Weisdale and Tresta. She felt the Bixter section was a bit uninteresting, but when they passed the Brig o' Walls and came on to the narrow, winding section which was the last lap to Sandness she felt she was coming home. For a little girl in those days a holiday in the country was an exciting business. Her return fare was two shillings (10p)!

Life on the croft out in Sandness was fascinating and full of interest. There were a number of children in the immediate neighbourhood, and she soon made friends with them. When she was a little older she would join them in their daily task of driving the cows up to the communal pasture in the mornings, and fetching them down again at night. One cow was tethered by itself in a field near the house, and, once she was able to pull up the stake and drive it down again with the aid of a big stone, it became her task to carry out the daily flitting of the cow.

When she was still very small she played 'hoosie' out in the yard at Sandness, and often wondered why Aunty Lizzie didn't grow more flowers. It took her a while to realise that Aunty was always so busy that she never had time for anything like growing flowers. Every year there was at least one caddy lamb, and every year Inga and the caddy became great friends. She realised that the lamb's devotion was largely inspired by the fact that it was always given a piece of Inga's digestive biscuit, but the cuddly lambs were the only pets she ever knew, and she prized the relationship greatly. Every year there was the hay to work in. That was always good fun, and when the fields with the hay were some distance from the house, as soon as they saw a white flag appearing on the peatstack they all knew that was Aunty's signal that dinner was ready, and that they were to return forthwith.

The peats also needed a lot of work, and whole days would be spent away up in the hill. Sometimes it was almost like a picnic, for Uncle would get a fire going, boil a kettle and make tea. Then they would all sit around and eat their sandwiches. Small girls couldn't be expected to work all day non-stop, so there would be breaks while she picked the berries which proliferated up the hill among the heather.

Perhaps what she enjoyed most was when Uncle took her off with him in his boat. She remembered the first time he had said to her,

"Inga, wid doo laek ta com aff ta da eela wi me?" She knew what 'da eela' was, but she had no idea what it would be like. But from her earliest days she had had an enquiring mind, and she had overheard Aunty saying one day, "Shö haes ta ken everything aboot everything." So now she didn't hesitate to say 'yes' to Uncle. This would be a new experience. And so it proved. This was more exciting than anything she had ever done - off in a boat! Uncle had two of the neighbours with him, and one of them rigged a dorrow for her and showed her how to use it. Five flies were attached to the end of the line, and after he had dropped this over the side he placed the line in her hands and instructed her.

"Just lat da line rin oot a bit, dan stop hit, an wirk dee haand back and fore ta keep da flees muvvin in da watter." Soon she had the rhythm, then suddenly the line was almost snatched from her hand.

"Hadd on, hadd on," her mentor cried. "Doo's gotten a piltock. Start haulin in dee line noo." Inga complied, but found it hard work, with the line being particularly harsh on her soft hands. She never knew that a piltock could be as srong as this! Finally, she had her catch alongside - there were two piltocks sprickling in the water, not just one. Her friend lifted them aboard - she looked at them threshing about and wondered how she was going to get them off the hooks.

"Hit's aa richt," said Robbie, "Ah'll kavel dem fur dee." That was a new word for her, but he proceeded to take the hooks out of her catch, so she added the word to her vocabulary. Thus initiated into the practicalities of fishing, she made many more trips to 'da eela', but secretly it was the fun of going off in a boat rather than the fishing which drew her. The task of removing fish from the hooks was not something that she ever came to enjoy.

Coming ashore from a fishing trip always produced its own special ceremony. The boat having been hauled up, the fish were taken out and then carefully divided among the crew. Three men, so there were three shares, and as each fish was allocated in turn to each of the small piles, great care was taken to ensure that, as near as possible, each share received a fish of comparable size. "Een ta dee, een ta dee an een ta me," the divider would say. Invariably two cats appeared on the scene, as if they had been watching for the boat's appearance. They sat, never taking their eyes off the fish while the division was going on. Always they were rewarded for their patience with the allocation of a fish each, and, in the manner of cats everywhere, marched arrogantly off with their prizes as being no more than their due.

Sometimes Uncle took the whole family into Papa. Inga loved the island, it seemed so green and welcoming. She was very conscious that this was where her mother had been born, but that house was now empty and falling into disrepair. There were still some relations left on the island though, and Aunty Lizzie took her to visit them. One day, on the way back to Sandness, the wind came up and the sea quickly roughened. Uncle had to resort to quite a bit of tacking to make headway, and Inga enjoyed every minute of it, but Aunty had no love for small boats and the sea, and was frightened. Uncle was a matter-of-fact man, who had seen many a rough day in a boat. "Lass, Lizzie, dere's naethin to be faerd fur. Dis is just a bit o' a breeze."

Aunty was a good cook, and frequently baked bannocks - sometimes with beremeal - and oatmeal brunnies. One of these, spread with fresh butter straight from the kirn, was something special. There were two kirns - one the upright, plunge type, the other the round enclosed type where an interior paddle was turned by means of a exterior handle. Though she was too small to help with the upright model, Inga often helped by turning the handle on the other. There was always plenty of milk, and Inga drank pints and pints of it.

In the evenings Aunty would often go to visit neighbours, or, as it was called in those days, 'ta hadd her oot o' langor'. Always Inga was taken along, and, like all the other women, she would sit quietly knitting, saying nothing except when spoken to, but hearing everything - and puzzling over some of what she heard. The neighbours were always very kind to her, and she became like one of their own children. Always, before returning to town at the end of the holiday, she would go round the houses to say goodbye, and invariably she would receive some small present from these kind folk. Their gifts were usually money, and to someone like Inga she felt she was receiving riches.

She was into her teens on one trip to Sandness, and the war was in full swing. When she got on the little bus in Commercial Road and took her seat, she was aware there was a man sitting opposite her. When he began to sing, her attention was drawn to him, and she realised he had had a few. She also realised that he was a Norwegian. For the rest of the journey she sat in some trepidation, wondering just what this wild foreigner might do next. She was to realise later that she had no need to have worried. The wild Norskie was simply a boy on his way to Sandness to visit the girl he was later to marry. In the years ahead Inga always had the warmest of memories for the Sandness folk.

Chapter Six

SECONDARY SCHOOL

By 1939 Inga was embarking on her secondary school course, and, even as she did so, was uncomfortably aware that war was very near. By now George Blance was the school's headmaster. In 1936 they had come into school one morning, and, looking up, had seen Mr Blance and not Mr Durham standing on the balcony looking down on them. In their classroom it was clear that Miss Deyell had been weeping, and soon they all knew - Mr Durham was dead. The suddenness of his death left a lasting impression on them. It wasn't long until Mr Blance was confirmed in his position as headmaster of the school, a post he was to hold for the next thirty years.

Inga had been aware at the end of primary school that she would have no bother passing the Control Examination, which would have given her entry to the Anderson Institute. But she never even considered going to the Institute. The very fact of going there would have indicated that she had ambitions of going to university. There was no way her mother could face the additional expense that would involve. If she did go on, the only hope she had of coming back to Shetland was by becoming a teacher. Still painfully shy, Inga couldn't visualise herself ever standing up in front of a class to teach. She watched some of her friends depart for the Institute without any feelings of jealousy. It was OK for them - their parents could afford it - but fate had dealt her a different hand and she accepted it without rancour. And from the first she enjoyed her Commercial Course. This course included shorthand and typewriting, and, as she was sure by now that her future lay in office work, both were necessary. Brother John by this time was just finishing his similar three-year course.

After having had the same teacher for virtually all subjects in the primary, it was a marked change to find a different teacher for each subject in the secondary. Some of them impressed her. One of her favourite subjects was English, and here they had Jim Clark as their mentor. Jim was not everybody's cup of tea, Inga discovered, but she liked him because she instinctively understood that he was a really good teacher - the proof? - he made his lessons interesting. He made occasional forays into Latin or Greek to illustrate the roots of many of our words, and that fascinated her. Inga was beginning to realise that if she had the chance she would very much have enjoyed learning languages. They now began to get French, and that she lapped up. Their teacher here to begin with was Miss Irene Hughson, later to become Mrs Lamont, wife of Shetland's surgeon. She was succeeded by Miss Nancy Stewart, and they were very happy with her. For the really important part of the course, shorthand and typewriting, they had Miss Lena Mouat. She was a sound, impressive and kindly teacher, who imparted her subject with glowing results. Wilbert Tulloch taught them maths, but perhaps Inga was happiest in the music room, for music continued to be a powerful influence in her young life. Music always drew her like a magnet, and one night, hearing singing coming from the Central, she peeped in, to see and hear a rehearsal of 'Three Little Maids'. Three young ladies, all well-known in local musical circles - Kitty Gray, Jeannie Gray and Cissy Brown - were rehearsing the song. They were part of a group preparing a Gilbert and Sullivan production to be staged by the local Operatic Society. So for Inga was born a life-long enthusiam for Gilbert and Sullivan.

School life for Inga never presented any problems. For her it was a happy place. She had no difficulty with her lessons, she didn't get into trouble with her teachers, and she won prizes with great regularity. This she put down to the fact that she had a really excellent memory - "Anybody can win prizes if they have a good memory," she used to say. It took her a long time to accept that she was also extremely intelligent, though that was something her teachers well knew, even if she didn't. Time had smoothed out the grief which Dad's death had occasioned, thanks to their lodgers the family was paying its way, and as she entered her teens life had begun to feel really exciting.

Chapter Seven

War

Inga had not been long in the secondary when the day they had been dreading arrived. She was in church on the morning of 3rd September, 1939, when, from the wireless which had been set up to let everyone hear the Prime Minister's speech, Chamberlain's quavering voice made the dread announcement, "This country is now at war with Germany." Inga was very conscious of the solemnity of the occasion - the congregation sat in absolute silence after the broadcast. Some of them still had horrific memories of the First War, but for children like Inga it was the unknown which lay ahead. And the unknown can be full of fear. Just what would being at war mean? Just how could it affect Shetland? There had been so much talk on the wireless and in the papers about bombs and gas. Were they going to have them both raining down on them right away?

Already gas masks had been issued to everyone up at the Central School, and from now on the children would carry them to school with them every day. The cardboard containers which housed the masks were not very durable, and soon covers for the cartons were provided. It was more than a little intimidating to hear, from a loudspeaker mounted on a lorry which patrolled the streets, that all windows had to be blacked out after dark -

no gleam of light must be allowed to show outside. Failure to ensure this was an offence and would be punished. Soon wardens were patrolling the town to ensure that the rule was being strictly observed. Mom improvised blackouts from sheets, though later they had got some black cloth for the purpose. Perhaps the biggest fear in those early days was gas. The grownups clearly dreaded the possibility, and that fear communicated itself to the children. Civil Defence people were being given training in how to deal with gas, and at school they had to practice putting on their gas-masks and learning to work with them on. They hated it.

The excitement engendered by the declaration of war kept everyone at a high pitch for a few days, but nothing much happened, children are very resilient, and gradually life took on a normal pattern once again, the only really big change being the blackout. But then troops started arriving with every trip of the steamer. Early incomers were the Argylls, the Black Watch and the Highland Light Infantry, and to begin with they were under canvas at the Point of Skattland. But winter was almost upon them, and, however remote the brasshats might be, it was accepted that life under canvas in Shetland in winter would be tough, so gradually the gutters' huts were pressed into service as barracks, right in to Sutherland's station at the foot of Brown's Road. Inga's bedroom window looked right down on these huts. As the numbers of soldiers grew, their presence became a feature of town life. They marched up to the Garrison for their meals, and they drilled at the foot of the Town Hall Brae and in St Olaf Street outside St Clements. Their trucks, Bren Gun Carriers and rhythmic marching feet became part of the everyday scene.

Inga was interested in all that was going on, but it was brother John who became immersed in all the war's happenings. In his bedroom he had a map of the world pinned up on the wall, and little red pins denoted places where something eventful had taken place. One of the soldiers had become a very good friend of the family, and often visited the house. From somewhere he had procured a wireless set and gifted it to them. Now John could keep track of everything that was reported from the various theatres of war, Inga at last could enjoy some of the music which, even in wartime, was regularly broadcast, and Mom could listen to the Sunday broadcast.

John's pins kept going in, and for a while the one denoting the demise of the *Graf Spee* held the pride of place. Often he spoke to Inga about the war, and how this was a war they must win, for if they lost, all freedom would be lost. Inga understood this full well, but, though John was a big boy now, she always felt glad he was too young to get involved on active service. She knew Mom, too, was grateful for that, but what they both overlooked was that John was sixteen in 1940, and five feet ten inches tall, weighed nearly twelve stones, and was to all intents a man. Having finished his Commercial Course he had found employment in an office - but most of the time his thoughts were far away from Lerwick.

The first time the war really came home to them was on 22nd November, 1939. They had all come out of school for the dinner hour, and a large number of children, including Inga, thronged King Harald Street, about to make their way both north and south for their mid-day meal. Suddenly there was the noise of aircraft engines, and a number of planes could be seen coming in low from the direction of the Waari Geo. They flew very low right north over King Harald Street. So low were they that the children, looking up, could clearly see the pilots, and they waved to the men at the controls. The planes flew on over the excited children, who had all clearly seen the black crosses on their sides. This was early in the war, a plane over Lerwick was still a very unusual sight, and for most of the bairns the thought that these might be the enemy never entered their heads. A few of the more worldly wise quickly spread the word, and then the sound of machine-guns could be heard as the planes sank a flying-boat in the north harbour. For the children the reality of the danger they had been in didn't fully register, but for parents, when they heard the story, there was nothing but deep thankfulness. Had the planes opened-up with machine-guns on the street full of children, it would have been a day of such tragedy as Shetland had never known in all its history.

From then onwards German planes paid frequent visits to Shetland, and now, whenever aircraft engines were heard, everyone assumed that they were German. The air-raid sirens now gave timely warning, and on their sounding, the children in school were immediately evacuated to the playsheds, where banks of sandbags had been piled to give protection from possible blast. Long spells in air-raid shelters could be extremely boring and claustrophobic, too, for children, but some of the teachers displayed considerable initiative. Ella McWilliam, for instance, taught the girls dancing. For the most part they had to manage without music, but that made no difference - they learned the steps. As far as Inga was concerned, learning to dance was much more pleasant, than worrying about German planes being overhead. Indeed, she usually forgot completely why they were in the sheds, and gave herself up wholly to enjoying the dancing. In these days, too, the music room took on a new atmosphere, for they began to sing tunes like 'The Siegfried Line', 'Roll out the Barrel', 'Run, Rabbit, Run', and others of the popular wartime songs.

So in the early days war didn't touch Inga very much. She was aware that Shetlanders were being lost at sea, but so far tragedy had not touched any of those near and dear to her. Then they heard on the radio, on 9th April, 1940, that the Germans had invaded Denmark and Norway, and almost immediately, it seemed, the war came close. British naval ships, badly damaged in action on the Norwegian coast, limped into harbour, showing clear signs that lives had been lost on board them. It was only now that measures were taken to seal off the harbour front, which, until now, had been as open and unrestricted as in the days of peace. Perhaps most disturbing was the arrival of refugees from Norway. They were taken to Sutherland's huts at the foot of Brown's Road, and now Inga's bedroom window looked directly down on these newcomers. None of them stayed there very long before they were put on board the steamer to start their journey to London where they would be thoroughly screened. She heard it said that there were some 'bad' Norwegians among the refugees. A man called Quisling was often mentioned, and it seemed that it was believed that many of his followers were 'bad' Norwegians.

Sometimes one or two of the Norwegians would come up to the back fence, and John and Inga would go down and try and communicate with them. But they spoke no English and John and Inga spoke no Norwegian, so it all came down to sign language, and that was never very satisfactory. But Inga listened as they spoke Norwegian amongst themselves, and was intrigued.

"John, Ah'm gaun ta laern ta spaek yon language some day. Efter aa, dey're wir nearest neebors." "Kennin dee Inga, I hae little doot doo will," said John.

But there was much more to the situation now than just refugees and damaged ships. The authorities publicly warned that an invasion by Germans from Norway would come at any moment, and everyone accepted that this was highly likely. So much so, in fact, that they were sent home from church one morning with the information that the Germans were on their way, and would be landing very shortly. They waited, but the Germans did not appear. In common with most other folk Inga wondered what would happen when the enemy arrived. "Whit will dey dö ta wis, John?" Inga wondered.
"I dunna suppose dey'll pey much attention ta wis, Inga," John replied. "Bit doo kens dey're been sikker on da Poles, an dere's aa sorts o' stories aboot whit geens on in yon camps dey're set up in Germany fur whit dey caa political prisoners. As far as I kin mak oot hit's da Jews it dey dislaek maist. Dere's wan thing fur sure - we're no Jews!"
But the fear of the invasion continued, and Lerwick people were called out to dig a deep trench right round the town - it was said the Earl of Cork believed this would stop the tanks.

In London, Shetland suddenly assumed a position of considerable importance in the eyes of the powers-that-be. No way could the islands be allowed to fall into German hands. Almost immediately more troops began to pour into the islands - so many that the North boats simply couldn't cope, and troop-ships had to be allocated to provide the necessary transport from Invergordon to Lerwick. Soon the garrison troops were as numerous as the island's inhabitants - indeed, probably more numerous. What had been a moderate military presence quickly became a dominant factor in everyday life, and military camps sprang up all over the place. Soon Nissen huts could be numbered in their hundreds. Many of the camps were in and around the town, but many more were in country areas. Overnight, almost, the whole character of the town seemed to change.

By this time the news had come that the Germans had driven westwards into the Low Countries, and in no time at all, it seemed, came the news of the miracle of Dunkirk. It was good news that the bulk of the British army escaped, but there was no disguising the fact that Britain had suffered a terrible defeat, and the fall of France meant that the Germans were sitting just over twenty miles from the south coast of England. Britain stood alone, and now the danger of a German invasion of the south of England seemed much more real than a possible German attack on Shetland. Shetlanders breathed a sigh of relief that their own immediate danger seemed to have passed, but they realised only too clearly that Britain herself was in danger.

Losses at sea to ships of the merchant navy reached terrible totals, and there were many Shetlanders at sea in the merchant navy. Almost every day came the news of someone lost, and now the war became very personal, for at school there was always someone's father or brother or uncle had been drowned or was missing. That was the worst, Inga always thought, not to know whether a loved one was alive or dead. One morning her best friend, Mary, came to school in tears.
"Whit's wrang, Mary?" Inga asked anxiously.
"Hit's Dad's ship. We're hed wird fae da owners dat his ship, da *Braemoor*, has been sunk 'by enemy action'. Dey dunna ken if dere's ony survivors."
"Dat's terrible, Mary. Is dat aa you ken?"

"We ken day wir on dir wye hame fae Argentina, so we tink hit's laekly been in da sooth Atlantic at dey wir sunk. Does doo tink ony o' dem will hae been saved, Inga?"

Inga had no more idea than her friend, but she knew that what was needed now was comfort and hope.

"Ah'm sure dere wir survivors, Mary," she said. "Da Germans ir no evil bruits - dey'll hae taen da crew on board dir ain ship. You'll mebbe hae ta be patient, fur you'll laekly hear nae wird till dey're taen tae a prison camp in Germany. Ah'm heard dat da merchant navy men ir aa taen tae a camp awa up near Hamburg." She spoke with as much assurance as she could muster - a thirteen-year-old wise in the ways of war through listening to a big brother who was indeed well informed. Mary's tears were dried - hope had been rekindled with the maxim that no news was good news - and the girls took their place in class as usual.

So people adjusted as best they could to war-time life. But Inga became increasingly aware of John's preoccupation with the war. As he approached his seventeenth birthday, he revealed his thoughts increasingly to Inga, whom he was now treating as an equal in age.

"Doo kens, Inga, Ah'm big enoff ta join up, an Ah'm shör if I said I wis auld enoff dey wid takk me."

"Oh, John, doo doesna hae ta geen till doo'd called up. Be dat time da war'll shörly be ended. Whit wid Mom feel if doo left noo?"

"I ken - an hit's dat at worries me. Hit's shör ta hit her badly whin I geen. Bit Ah'm feelin mair an mair at I hae ta geen."

Inga worried and hoped that he wouldn't do anything rash. She dreaded what it would do to Mom if he went away to the war. But her worst fears were realised when John, on his seventeenth birthday, announced that he was going to 'sail'. He was sure he would be accepted into the merchant navy without question, for shipping losses had become so heavy that the situation was bordering on desperate. As he said to Inga, "Dey're needin every man dat dey kin git. Da loss o' sae mony ships will mebbe staerve wis ta defeat - bit hit's da loss o' sae mony crews as weel dat's sae critical. I man geen." Of course Mom was very upset. Both she and Inga pleaded with John to wait. But it was soon clear that his mind was made up - and when John's mind was made up nothing would shift him. So Mom and Inga tried to put a brave face on it, but it seemed no time at all till they were down on the pier waving to John as the *Magnus* steamed south the harbour and disappeared. A lot of tears were shed by the two Johnson women that night. They weren't very far from John's eyes too, as he lay in his comfortless bunk in the steerage of the North boat.

But it wasn't long till a letter arrived telling Mom and Inga that John had signed on aboard the *Dunkeld*, and was setting sail shortly. For security reasons that was the only detail he gave them. Nothing was said about where they were going.

Chapter Eight

The School In War

Since Dad's death Mom had been increasingly reliant on John as the man of the house. He had excellent hands, and made light of all the small jobs about the house that required expert attention. His departure left both Mom and Inga devastated, and even little sister seemed to share their feelings. Mom was slow to come to grips with John's absence. For her it was a case of her man dead, and her son gone into danger from which he might very well never return. But the young are resilient, and soon Inga was looking forward to the occasional letters that came from him, and was writing frequently to keep him posted on all that was happening at home.

At school things continued to go well, and she was slowly but surely growing older. Secondary One had given way to Secondary Two, and already she was beginning to look forward to the end of school days and the beginning of work and earning a wage. The blackout was a nuisance - and soon it was difficult to find a shop which stocked batteries for torches, and torches were essential in the blackout, although you were allowed to show only a very narrow beam of light. The curfew, which began at 11 pm, didn't affect her much as she was still too young to be going to dances and other entertainment. The wardens continued to patrol the streets, and there was always the occasional shout of "Pit yon licht oot!" John's letters were often exciting, because after he came back from a voyage, he would describe places he had visited, and Inga felt that, though every trip he made was dangerous, he was seeing a lot of the world.

The year 1942, which was to see the end of her school life, was an eventful year. The Institute was taken over to serve as a hospital, and all the Institute pupils had to be found accommodation in the Central. This was a tall order, for the Central roll was really all the school could cope with in normal circumstances. Now classrooms had to be divided to make each into two rooms, while some primary classes had to be farmed out to the U. F. Church, the Methodist schoolroom and even the Bruce Hostel, from which resident country girls had been evacuated and found digs in houses in the town. It was here that the Earl of Cork and Orrery set up his H.Q. as Commander of Orkney and Shetland. In the Central the two sets of pupils and the two staffs had to learn to live and work with each other in very crowded conditions.

At that time, at least in the minds of the town's schoolbairns, there was always a very real gulf between the Institute and the Central. Perhaps it was inevitable that that sort of attitude should have arisen, for the Institute pupils in the main formed a sort of intellectual élite - after all, weren't they at the Institute because they had passed the Control exam? When the two schools came together, that attitude had to be tempered to fit the needs of the situation, and it has to be said that the two schools co-existed in these difficult times with a minimum of friction. Inga paid little attention to differences either imagined or real - she did hear one of the older Institute girls being referred to as a 'toffee-nosed bitch', and human nature being what it is, she didn't like being referred to in disparaging tones as a 'Centralite', but none of it was important enough to make any impression. By and large she felt that the Central pupils probably had a feeling of inferiority because their school was only a three-year secondary whereas the Institute was a six-year. That didn't worry her.

By this time the Central gymnasium and technical block had been requistioned by the army for hospital purposes, and all PT was carried out in the school hall. On top of all the overcrowding there was now some army instruction being provided in the school, and Inga could remember soldiers standing at the balcony rail watching as they did their PT. She was beginning to realise that she was no longer a bairn but a growing lass, and that it is in the nature of soldiers to look at lasses whenever the opportunity arises. That didn't stop her being embarrassed under the scrutiny of these uniformed young men. After school there would be hockey practices up at Bellevue, and here Institute and Central girls would mingle, with the older Institute girls playing leading roles.

In due course the Garrison became a much renovated place of entertainment under the name of The Garrison Theatre. It housed entertainment of all sorts for the troops, and it drew some of the children like a magnet. Along with some of her friends Inga would peep in the big main door to see what was going on. The soldiers in charge were often very understanding, and one night Inga and two of her friends were allowed to stand for a little while in the side aisle and watch the show going on on the stage. It was a pantomime and they had never seen a pantomime before. It was all very strange with some of the male characters masquerading as women and with a girl dolled up as a Prince. The soldier audience laughed uproariously at the jokes, but the girls didn't think them very funny because they didn't understand them. But the atmosphere of a stage show appealed to them very much, and from then on they eagerly accepted any chance that came their way to go to a show in the Garrison.

Pictures were shown in the Garrison on Sundays. One Sunday - by this time she was in Secondary Three - Inga and her pal Mary were invited by the soldiers to come and see the picture. No way was it an easy matter on which to reach a decision.
"Hit's Sunday, Inga. Dy midder'll nivir lat dee geen ta da pikters on a Sunday - doo kens dat!" Inga knew the truth of that only too well. The Garrison pictures on a Sunday? Never! That would undoubtedly be classed as a major sin. She knew fine well what her mother's attitude would be, but she had heard of the film which was to be shown. It was a musical, and she simply loved musicals. She pondered the matter lengthily. She wasn't yet fifteen, but she had a mind of her own, and she was clear in her own mind that to ban films on a Sunday was unreasonable and narrow-minded. She was conscious that many of the time-honoured Sunday strictures were disappearing before the needs of war-time life, and as she said to Mary, "I dunna see onybody bein laid flat be da haand o' da Loard!" Finally, "Ah'm med me mind up. We'll geen ta da pikters, dan efter I cum haem Ah'll tell Mom Ah'm been. Shö'll be awful mad, bit hit'll be ower late dan ta dö much aboot hit."

In the summer holidays , between Secondary Two and Secondary Three, Inga got a job working in the library for a short time, and for that she received the - to her - magnificent wage of £1-10/- a week (£1.50). This was the first wage she ever received, and she savoured the excitement of holding so much money in her hand! She was still knitting whenever she had a spare moment, and by this time she was a really good knitter. She stuck mainly to gloves - a pair of mens' plain gloves gave her a return of 1/9 (9p), and a pair of Fair Isle 2/6 (12.5p) Then, during term time she got a Saturday morning job with Alexandra Bakery, and for that she was paid 5/- (25p). Mom's sewing machine kept going as busily as ever, the lodgers still lodged, and letters came from John, often with some money in them. So the Johnsons managed. Then granny died, and now there was just Inga, Mom and peerie Ellen. What it did mean was that Inga at last had a room of her own.

As the weeks passed Inga reached her fifteenth birthday. She was probably the last one to be conscious of it, but the peerie schoolbairn had given way to a very pretty young girl. She had already realised that she was never going to be very big, but that was something which never worried her. She discovered early on that being small can very often be turned to one's advantage. As she used to say to Mary, "Whin you're peerie you just hae ta look helpless an somebody'll aye cum an gie you a haand". Music remained one of the great loves of her life, along with dancing. The visit by Gracie Fields was a red-letter day - Gracie sang to the crowd outside the Garrison, and Inga was one of the crowd, needless to say. And even if you're still not fifteen, being in Secondary Three means that you're nearly an adult, and adults can go to concerts and dances. The first dance was an adventure for Inga and Mary. They made their entrance somewhat gingerly, and were conscious that they were probably the youngest there. They were quite prepared to dance with each other, but that didn't last long. Thanks to the school play-sheds and the air-raid warnings, they were both excellent dancers, and the boys soon spotted that. Then they were quickly in demand for every dance.

At the end they stuck together. They knew that boys escorted girls home after dances, but they were hardly ready for that yet. The mere fact that they had been to their first dance was excitement enough for one night. Mary lived in one of the new Council house in Haldane Burgess Crescent, and Inga kept her company as far as Pete's. As she walked back to her own home in Commercial Road in the darkness of the blackout, she mused to herself that, despite the thousands of strange men in uniform who now lived in Shetland, she had no dread of being out by herself late at night, and even her mother, with all her worries, never forbade her to go.

Chapter Nine

School Ends

In 1942 Inga reached her fifteenth birthday, and in the same year she left school. Leaving school was quite a wrench, for she had enjoyed school life, and all her friends were there. Of course they, too, would be leaving, and they too, were feeling the uncertainty of entering a new world. It was war-time, and there were jobs for virtually all the school-leavers. Those who had done a Commercial Course automatically looked for work in offices. Inga had never had any money, and her family had never had more than just enough to live on. Perhaps that was why her ambition was to work in a bank. Her performance in the Commercial Course had been such that she could have her pick of the jobs which were on offer, and, without hesitation, she plumped for a vacancy in one of the banks. She was sent down to be interviewed by the manager, and of course that prospect loomed as being quite an ordeal. But the manager turned out to be a nice man, and, shy though she was, she soon found herself at her ease. One of his questions was, "Why do you want to work in a bank?" Her reply, which seemed to cause him some amusement, was, "I think I would like to work with money." After she said it, she wondered if he would think she was just showing herself to be a greedy little so and so. How could she explain that it wasn't that she dreamed of having a lot of money - it was just that money was something she had always wanted to work with - to count, to put in columns of figures and extract totals which she was sure would be correct. The manager's interested questions drew something of this from the nervous young girl, and by the time the interview was finished, he was satisfied that she would make an excellent addition to his staff. Her shyness intrigued him, for behind it he could see the pulsing ability just waiting to show itself.

Before she left he had told her that the job was hers, and he looked forward to welcoming her to the bank on Monday morning. Once out in the street she felt like dancing. The very job she had always wanted was hers! Her new boss was a nice man. "I tink Ah'll laek wirkin fur him," she thought to herself. "Ah'll hae ta geen haem an tell Mom. Sho'll nivir believe me." She had not told Mom that she was going for a bank interview that morning, and now she almost ran all the way home to Commercial Road, bursting in on her mother with the momentous news.
"Inga - doo's gaun ta wirk in a bank? Does doo tink doo'll be able ta dö dat? Doo's nivir hed ony money ta wirk wi."
"Mom, Ah'm aye wanted ta wirk in a bank. I kinna explain hit, bit hit's just somethin Ah'm aye wanted ta dö".
"Hit'll be real jantry at doo'll be mixin wi in yon job. Foo tinks doo will doo be able ta git on wi dem? Doo's nivir seen onything very jantrified in wir hoose, doo kens!"
"Ah'll laekly feel laek a fish oot o' watter ta begin wi, Mom, an doo kens foo shy I im. Bit dey're just human beins laek wis, an Ah'm no gaun ta be faerd fur dem. Efter aa, I hae a grain o' wit mesel." Brave words, she knew, but she had got the job she wanted - she had no intention of surrendering it without a fight.

Now there was the question of what she would wear to work. To buy a new outfit was out of the question for two reasons - one, there wasn't enough money, and, two, clothing needed coupons and they had very few. Whatever Inga had earned with her Saturday job had gone in the house expenses, with only a small part kept for her own use. But she had accumulated several pairs of gloves to sell, and, one way and another, she found that she could at least run to a new pair of shoes, new stockings and a few other odds and ends. Mom's sewing machine also worked overtime, and when, on Monday morning, she set out in good time to report to the bank, complete with white blouse, jacket, skirt and new shoes, she looked every bit the young business woman setting out for work. The manager greeted her when she entered the bank, and she felt pretty sure that he regarded her with approval as he cast a quick but penetrating glance over her outfit.

The first day seemed to pass in a dream. She had always picked things up very quickly, and she missed nothing of what she was told and shown. Her shyness prevented her ever seeming bumptious or over-confident, and the people who would be her colleagues quickly began to feel that the new girl would be no trouble, and might, indeed, soon be very useful. For Inga, her opinions about the rest of the staff were quickly formed. There was one young fellow of whom she would be extremely wary, but the rest were friendly people whom she liked immediately, and who were clearly quite prepared to accept her. She was, of course, by far the youngest member of staff, but that was a feeling that soon left her. She came home after work full of news to tell Mom, and also full of excitement. For Mom, her little girl had entered a world which was quite alien to her, and she could only listen in wonderment to Inga's excited stories. She well remembered her days 'in service', and her place in the scheme of things relative to the moneyed family for which she worked. Now here was Inga working more or less as an equal with a similar class of people. Could any good come of it? At the back of her mind was the old feeling, born of the lanes, "Yon's no fur da laeks o' wis," but she held her wheest, and tried to share in her girl's obvious happiness.

It wasn't just her new work with which Inga had to come to terms. It was suddenly borne in on her that she was no longer a schoolgirl. As she came in along Commercial Road in the mornings she began to feel that, in a way, she was having to run the gauntlet. There were always small groups of young men engaging in early morning chats on their way to work at the Malakoff, etc., and clearly they were beginning to see her with suddenly interested eyes. She knew a number of them, but that didn't make it any better when the wolf whistles sounded from the other side of the street, and when mildly suggestive remarks were called across to her as she passed. She knew there was no ill-will in all the banter, but her shyness made it very hard for her to take it in her stride. Frequently, in order to avoid the morning chorus, she would go up Market Street, along Hillhead and down the lane to the bank. She still hardly realised that she was now old enough to be an object of interest and admiration to male eyes. She overheard a boy saying one day, "Peerie Inga Johnson is gittin ta be a rael nice bit o' stuff," but the overheard comment, though pleasing in a way, was at the same time embarrassing.

Leaving school and starting work was like entering a new life. For a time Inga was very conscious that she was the newest and youngest employee in the bank. But she quickly came to grips with the work which her post involved, and, though not yet sixteen, gave an impression of considerable maturity. Things were different at home, too, for with her new-won independence she found Mom's strictures had less and less effect on her life. In any case peerie Ellen was now taking up much more of her Mom's attention, for she was now a school bairn in her early days at school. Inga and Mary had similar interests, and now they shared in nearly all the ploys and adventures on which they embarked. Mary, too, had a good singing voice, and they found themselves frequently performing duets at social evenings and such-like. They both loved dancing, and with no shortage of dances in the Town Hall, the Grand and the Masonic, there was never any difficulty in finding somewhere to go. And of course war-time in Lerwick was a time of plenty for the girls, for the town was full of young men in uniform, in the main a mixture of English, Scottish and Welsh. Most of the Shetland boys were themselves away in uniform. There were other young men from foreign lands including Poland and Norway, and the young Norwegians came to find a special place in Inga's heart.

Chapter Ten

A Foreign Connection

Almost from the day Norway was invaded there had been a Norwegian presence in the refugee camp down below Inga's bedroom window. The Johnsons had grown quite accustomed to having these people living there, but none of them ever stayed long enough in the camp for any real friendships to be established, even had they been able to speak each other's language. But things changed when the Norwegian MTBs came to Lerwick in November, 1942. They had their own camp, canteen and workshop at the Anglo-Scottish, and their own blacksmith at the Malakoff. With eight MTB crews, and a sizeable number of shore personnel, the permanent Norwegian presence in the town was considerable.

It was when a Norwegian girl had started to attend the Central that Inga's real connection with the Norwegians began. The little girl's name was Ingrid Hovden, and she could speak hardly any English. Though they were considerably older, Inga and Mary tried to help in making the little girl feel at home, and they gradually learned that the whole Hovden family was in Lerwick. The father and four of the boys were on the MTBs, while the youngest boy was not yet fifteen, but impatiently waiting the day when he, too, could become a crew member on an MTB.

Father Hovden was a pilot on the boats, and mother Hovden workied in the Norwegian Officers' mess. After a time the family was given accommodation in Hope Villa in St Olaf Street, and it was there that Inga and Mary got to know the Hovden boys - Oskar, who had escaped to Shetland in 1941 - Jon, Arne, Inge and Lars. Oskar was already married, but the others were all foot-loose and fancy free. Their trips to the Norwegian coast were inevitably always fraught with danger, and the euphoria of their safe return to port was usually followed by a carefree celebration ashore. The girls soon became familiar with the Norwegian customs, and were interested spectators on May 17th, the Norwegian National Day, when the Norwegians in the town staged a big parade, just as they would have done at home in Norway. Ingrid had pride of place in the procession, mounted on a little Shetland pony. Mrs Hovden prepared various national dishes, most of which Inga enjoyed, but she had difficulty acclimatising to bread and jam with cheese on top.

The war made its presence felt in Lerwick in a very real way in January, 1942, when mines exploded at the Waari Gio and at the Slates. Though they heard the explosions clearly enough, there was no damage to Inga's part of the town, though the houses in the vicinity of the blasts suffered badly, and even the Central School did not escape. The schoolbairns heard with sorrow that Warden Walter Jamieson had been killed by the blasts. In April, 1943, there was an explosion quite near to Inga's home, when a faulty mine exploded on board one of the MTBs lying at the Anglo-Scottish. One Norwegian was killed and four injured, among them young Lars Hovden. He had been taken on as an apprentice with the shipwrights until he was old enough to go to sea. Badly injured, he was taken to the Institute hospital, where he was regularly visited by his family and occasionally by Inga and Mary. His injuries were such that he had to be taken to Edinburgh for specialist treatment, but he finally made a complete recovery and joined his brothers on the MTBs.

The presence of the little boats was even more seriously felt in November, 1943, when there was an explosion on a British MTB lying at the Anglo-Scottish alongside a Norwegian MTB. Both boats blazed furiously, and eight men died with a number more injured. Lerwick didn't escape, for, in Inga's part of town, many windows were broken and numerous roofs damaged. The Johnsons and many more were evacuated, and kept away until it was certain there would be no more explosions.
"We just gude ta me Aunty's in King Harald Street. I dunna suppose dat wis very sensible fur some o' da hooses dere hed lost windows as weel," said Inga.

One way or another the girls had increased contact with the Norwegians. The fact that many of the strangers were learning to speak English made the process a lot easier. Apart from a few words, Inga didn't learn Norwegian, but as she listened to them chattering away in their own language, she told herself that this was a language she could easily learn.
"Some day I **will** learn it," she promised herself. By this time she was feeling settled at the bank, and with her steadily increasing age, she and Mary were now very much more confident when they went to dances. Now there were actually girls younger than they were who were beginning to come!

With increasing age came increasing physical maturity, and both girls began to realise that they were attracting increased masculine attention. The Norwegians were popular with both of them, but the Hovdens remained the ones they knew best. Inga asked them once what part of Norway they came from.

" We come from the island of Hovden," they replied. She felt they had not understood her question, and she asked them again, only to get the same answer. It dawned on her that their surname and the name of their island were the same, and with more experience she was to find numerous additional examples of the same thing. There were Englishmen, Scotsmen and Welshmen at the dances, sometimes even Poles as well, and nearly all of them had an eye for a pretty girl. These wartime days could be heady days for young girls, with several males for every female in the town. Fortunately both Inga and Mary were endowed with considerable common-sense and, though relishing the attention they received from the opposite sex, managed to steer a reasonably safe course through the many male pitfalls. Of course they were offered escorts home from the dances, and of course they accepted when they thought it was safe to do so. But when they had doubts about the individual who was making the offer, they would immediately team up, and the escort would find that the girls were inseparable, and both would disappear down the steps when they reached Inga's gate.

Inevitably there came the night when Mary was propositioned by a prospective escort about whom she knew very little, and came up with the standard response for such a situation.

"No, I'm sorry, but I'm here with my friend Inga, and we always go home together."

"Oh, that's all right. I'm here with my friend, too. He will take Inga home." And so it happened, but the girls maintained close contact on the walk home, and both disappeared down Inga's steps at the cost of a hurried smoorikin or two.

Chapter Eleven

Big Brother

The fact that John was always in danger was something that was ever-present in Inga's mind, but his letters kept coming, and she kept writing, and her worries decreased a little. She knew that shipping losses were continuing at a frightening rate, and there were innumerable stories of Shetlanders who had been on board ships that were torpedoed, or mined or bombed. She came home from the bank one afternoon, opened the door and went in, to be swept off her feet by a young man whom she realised suddenly was John. She was so delighted to see him that she didn't think to ask him why he was home - she just assumed he was on leave.

But then she couldn't help noticing that her mother didn't seem so excited as she had expected her to be with John home.
"Whit's wrang, Mom? Whit wye is doo no delighted ta see John?"
"Just ask him why he's haem, Inga."
"Whit is it, John? Whit's happened?"
And then she heard the story. John's ship had been returning from a voyage to America, and had come up the Channel and was entering the Thames Estuary. Suddenly there was a violent explosion up forard - they had hit a mine, even though they had

been following a channel which a mine-sweeper had cleared on the previous evening. The ship started to go down almost immediately, but the crew managed to get one boat launced and the rafts cast loose. Miraculously all the crew managed to get into the boat or on to rafts. There hadn't been a single casualty in the explosion when they hit the mine, and, according to John, "Hit wis nae time ava afore we wir picked up." He hadn't sent a telegram because he thought that would just worry them, but he had come north immediately and reached Aberdeen just before the north boat sailed.

"Hit cud happen ta onybody, an we wir very lucky. An here I im, safe an soond, so whit ir you aa worryin aboot? Ah'm gaun ta be haem fur at laest twa or tree weeks, an Ah'm gaun ta enjoy mesel, so lat's hae nae mair lang faces." So saying he picked up Ellen, set her on his shoulders, and announced, "We're gaun fur a walk. Is doo comin, Inga?"

It was great in the days that followed to have John home again. Peerie Ellen, who was now old enough to appreciate having a big brother, never left him when she came home from school. Inga and Mary were told on the following night that he was coming with them to a dance in the Town Hall, and the girls proudly led him into the Hall with them, for John was now a tall, good-looking young man, whom any girl would be proud to have as an escort. He danced with both of them, but he danced with other girls, too, particularly, Inga noted, with Sheila Leask, who had been two classes above her at school. Sheila was a very pretty girl, and Inga had always liked her, so she watched then now with considerable approval. Her big brother was too good for just any old girl. But it was time that he had a proper girl-friend. At the end of the dance John said to them, "Will you twa be aa richt gaun haem yoursels? I hae a peerie bit o' business ta attend ta." "I hoop doo enjoys dee business," said

Mary with a knowing smirk, while Inga commented approvingly, "I tink shö's an awful nice bit o' business, John."

So the days passed quickly and happily, till suddenly it was time for John to be off again. In all the time he had been home he had said little about his life on the sea, though he had told them a lot about the distant places he had visited. But his departure left the house feeling terribly empty, and they all missed him desperately, especially peerie Ellen for whom he had become a personal hero. They waited impatiently for a letter to come, with word that he had signed on another ship. This time, his letter told them, it was a big freighter called the *Highcliffe*, and there were two other Shetlanders on board. So once more it was back to anxious waiting for news, and as they entered 1943 they were thankful to have a letter from John just after the New Year, to tell them that all was well, and that he was just about to sail on another voyage.

Then there was the usual silence, but they had become accustomed to that. January went by, but by mid-February they had still heard nothing. The worry which was ever-present began to grow, and daily Mom watched for the postman. Then, one Friday, two terrible things happened. A letter came from the owners of John's ship saying that the ship was overdue, and must now be presumed lost, and adding that they had no information as to whether there were any survivors. They would inform the Johnsons immediately if any further information became available. On the same day a news item in the 'Shetland Times' reported that three Shetlanders were missing from a ship which had been seen floating bottom up in far northern waters. One of the three Shetlanders was named as John Johnson, so it was immediately clear to Mom and Inga that the ship was the *Highcliffe*. The letter, combined with the item in the 'Times', left the Johnsons numb with grief. Inga tried to rally and find a vestige of hope somewhere.

"Mom, we dunna ken at aa da crew wis lost. Mebbe some o' dem got awa in wan o' da boats. We kinna gie up hoop." She knew fine well that the chance of John's escape was slim - and, even if the crew had got away, what chance would there have been for them in Arctic waters in winter. But she had to try and find some gleam of hope to lift Mom just a little, for her grief was leaving her nearly prostrate. Peerie Ellen, seeing the state her Mom was in, was in constant tears, endlessly demanding if John would not be coming home. Inga's own grief was very real and very deep, but she realised that it was going to be up to her to get the family through the next few difficult days. Somehow, she kept her feelings under control, and asserted firmly that they were not going to give up hope. Nobody had told them that John was lost, and until they did she was not giving up. There was every chance that he had got away in a boat - he was big and strong and would have done everything possible. It was a case now of waiting for word, and meanwhile they would get on with their lives.

Maybe it was the firmness with which she spoke, maybe her words rekindled hope in Mom's mind, but now the sobs of both Mom and Ellen eased, and Mom regained sufficient control to wipe her eyes and take peerie Ellen on her lap.

"Yea, Inga, doo's aye da sensible een. As doo says, we're no gaun ta gie up hoop yit. Come, Ellen, doo man geen back ta da skule. An, Inga, awa ta dye wark. Dey'll be winderin whit's com o' dee."

Satisfied that her mother was in control of herself again, Inga set out. In her own mind hope was almost extinguised, but if hope could keep her mother going, then she would make sure hope didn't die. That night she met Sheila. Sheila had seen the item in the 'Times', and when Inga saw the tears on Sheila's face, she realised how strong the link between her and John had become. Away from her family she let her own tears flow, and the two girls comforted each other for a little while. They admitted to each other that all real hope had gone.

The days passed and there was no news to lighten the gloom. In her heart Inga knew that John ahd gone, and now she felt sure that Mom was equally convinced, but had somehow aquired the strength to keep up a pretence. Peerie Ellen still talked frequently about "Whin John coms haem ----", and was the only one of the three to genuinely believe that that would happen.

They had a further letter from the *Highcliffe's* owners to say the ship had been on a voyage to Archangel with a cargo of supplies for the Russians, but it was now confirmed that she had been sunk, and there was still no word of any survivors. It therefore seemed that there could be no other conclusion than that she had been lost with all hands. The two Johnson women read the letter in stunned silence. Though they had both reached the same conclusion in their own minds, to see the stark words on paper killed whatever faint thread of hope they might have retained. Their feelings were too deep for words. They just hugged each other, while the tears ran down their cheeks. A happy little Ellen, dashing in and declaring, "Whin John coms haem Ah'm gaun ta git him ta tak me fur a walk aroond da Knab," added to the poignancy of the moment. Ellen's worried query, "Whit's wrang wi you baith at you're greetin?" found both of them producing ill-prepared answers.

When Inga looked back, she realised just how hellish were the next few days. She had her own grief to cope with, but she also had to provide the strength to keep her mother going. Mom was really hard hit - she was having great difficulty putting on some sort of face for the benefit of their lodger. Thankfully, he was an understanding, Shetland man, and appreciated just what the Johnsons were suffering. They held off telling peerie Ellen the harsh reality of the situation - there was plenty of time for that - but it was so difficult to respond to her happy, carefree ploys. Then Sheila called on Inga more and more, and her sadness, too, was very real. Clearly John had meant a lot to her.

In the bank Inga found it difficult to present her normal cheerful, happy front to her colleagues. Fortunately, the need for close attention to her work took her mind off their loss for some of the time, but she actually dreaded going home, for she knew how down her mother was, and she had not yet found a way of raising her out of her despondency. She returned from work one never-to-be-forgotten evening to be met at the gate by a small Ellen who was laughing and crying at the same time, and who was almost too excited to speak.

"Hurry up, Inga! Hurry up! I hae somethin ta shaw dee. Doo doesna ken whit it is," and she grasped Inga's hand to pull her along more quickly.

"Whit's gotten her inta dis state?" Inga wondered, but dutifully hurried along in response to Ellen's excited urging. In they went, and Ellen's shouted, "See! Dere!" drew her eyes to the chair in front of the window where sat - No, my God, hit canna be- hit is - Hit's John! and she threw herself towards him, flinging her arms around him, cuddling him, laughing, crying, trying to ask incoherent questions.

"Lass, Inga, aese in - doo'll trottle me if doo's no carefil - Ah'm blyde ta see de tö, doo kens." He put his arms around her and drew her close to him. "Ah'm draemed aboot dis twartree times ower da last couple o' monts or so," he said quietly. Inga looked over to where her Mom sat, her face illuminated by a big, beaming smile.

"Mom, whit is dis? Whaur's he com fae?"

John answered for himself. "Ah'm com fae Sullom Voe," he said. "Yea," said Mom. "A truck wi twa Norskies cam ta da gate wi him mebbe an oor sin syne. Afore doo aksis ony mair, he's been waitin fur dee comin hom so dat he can tell his story tae wis aa at da sam time."

Inga drew back and looked at her brother. Now she could see this was not the John she had known. It was still the same big brother, but he looked somehow shrunken - she realised that he had lost an awful lot of weight. In fact he was like a skeleton. His face had changed - there was an air about him that made you feel that here was someone who had seen the other side of hell.

"John, aa at Ah'm carin aboot enoo is dat doo's haem. Does doo realise at we tocht we wid nivir see dee again? An noo doo's here - dis is da best day o' my life. Mom, is he hed onythin ta aet? Doo kin see he's needin maet."

"We wir just waitin fur dee, Inga. Ah'm been across ta da butcher's, an whin he hard at John hed cum haem he lat me hiv a great chunk o' sassermaet. He kens dat's John's favourite. We hed used aa wir ration fur da week, bit he just rowed hit up an telled me, "Dat's fur John." He widna takk a penny fur hit. Wisna hit awfil gude o' him?"

So the tea was made ready, and they all sat round the table. John sat between Inga and Ellen, and they laughed and cried and kept touching him, just to make sure he was really there. John was clearly in a pretty weak condition, but he thoroughly enjoyed his favourite tea, although perhaps he didn't eat quite as much as usual. "My stamach is no laerned ta cope wi richt maet yit," he said. Inga told herself that all he needed now was some good food. She would make sure he got it. He had been forbidden to tell any of his story until tea was finished. Then they all sat around, a cushion was placed at John's back, and Inga instructed him, "Noo, tell wis dee story." Before he could start she suddenly uttered a cry. "Foo cud I be sae tochtless? Dunna start yit, John. I hae ta geen an fetch somebody at's grieved as muckle as wis sin we tocht doo wis daed - Sheila." And she went out the door like a flash. It seemed only a minute or two till she was back, accompanied by Sheila. This was Sheila's first visit to the Johnsons', and she came in shyly, but when she saw John her shyness vanished, and she ran to him, embracing him and kissing him with a fervour that left no one in any doubt about her feelings for the young man. As Inga noted, John's response was equally uninhibited. Once again the tears flowed - once again tears of happiness. Finally Inga took proceedings in hand.

"You twa kin sit tagidder an hadd haands, bit we're still no hard dye story, John. Noo at Sheila's here we can aa listen tagidder. So - cum on - fire away."

Chapter Twelve

John's Story

"Weel, I suppose you cood say hit started whin we crossed fae Liverpool ta Boston, an took on board a lodd o' tanks an crated aeroplanes. Dat wis a common enoff cargo an we tocht naethin o' it. Dere hed been a rumour at we were ta sail ta da Med an we wir lookin forard ta dat. Bit dan cam da oarder ta proceed ta Halifax, an we wir pretty sure dat meant anidder trip across da Atlantic - an laekly a lokk o' attention fae da U-boats. At Halifax we joined a lokk o' idder ships at wir gadderin ta mak a convoy. Whin dere wir mebbe forty o' wis we left port an formed up in da usual convoy lines ootside. We sailed fur several days, athoot ony sign o' U-boats, an dan suddenly da oarder cam fir ten o' wis ta brakk aff an proceed ta Iceland. Dat wis enoff ta tell wis whit lay ahead - Russia."

As John explained, no seaman was keen to be part of a Russian convoy. Apart from the U-boats and German bombers, the weather was probably an even worse enemy, with the formation of ice on a ship's upper-works being particularly dreaded. So serious could this become that there were numerous instances of the sheer weight of ice making ships so top-heavy that they turned turtle and sank. Anyway, having called at Iceland, the ships set off, one by one. All ten were modern ships, and all could achieve a steady speed of at least fifteen knots, so the naval authorities had decided to sail them unescorted and one at a time in the hope that their speed would be sufficient to save them from U-boat attack. Though each of them had a four-inch gun mounted forard, they didn't put a great deal of faith in being able to shoot their way out of an attack either by surface ships or by bombers.

"Everything gude fine fur da first twa days," said John. "We saw nae sign o' idder U-boats or planes. Dan, on da third moarnin, whin daylicht cam in, da skipper bekam suspeecious o' wir compass. He kent fine weel at whin you got ower near da Pole, da compass can be affected be magnetic pull, an he reckoned wir een wisna behavin richt. A glint o' sun dat sam efternun let da mate git da sextant oot, an he discovered at we wir steerin a coorse at wid takk wis far ower near da Pole. We wir supposed ta pass mebbe fifty miles ta da sudderd o' da sooth end o' Svalbard - dat's Spitzbergen, doo kens, Inga. Fur we kent by dis time at wir destination wis da White Sea an da port o' Archangel."

A new course was set which would take them past the south end of Svalbard, but the weather was steadily deteriorating, and there were no more glimpses of sun to give them their position. They were now having to rely solely on a compass which might or might not be accurate. Ice started forming on deck and the crew were kept busy chipping it away, and using hot-water hoses to try and shift it. So intense was the cold that the hot water from the hoses started freezing before it could go over the side. They sailed on, alone as far as they could see on the darkling ocean, with snow showers frequently reducing visibility to virtually nil. The only sign of life they saw was a German long-range bomber which circled them but did not attack.

"Dir cam a nicht whin me an anidder fellow wir da lookoots. Hit wis a raelly coorse nicht, an you cood hardly see your haand afore your face. Hit wis snawin, wi no a glint o' stars, far less da Mirry Dancers. We hedna seen sign o' dem fae we left Iceland. Suddenly, athoot da slichtest warning, we hit hard - sae hard at we wir baith flung ta da deck. We hed been plooin on at aboot fifteen knots, an at dat speed sho hat wi some force. Da skipper wis on da bridge richt away, an gae orders fur aa da lichts ta be switched on. Da engines wir pitten in reverse, at full pooer, bit sho didna move. Time an again he tried - no use. Da boys sent forard ta hae a look cam back an reported dat da ship wis takkin water fast - an we harly needed ta be telled dat, fur it wis plain ta everybody at we wir sinkin. Dir wis no option - da oarder wis geen fur everybody ta go ta dir boat stations an ta abandon ship. Da skipper shouted at he wis sure hit wis Svalbard we hed hit - whin we got away fae da ship we wir ta steer nort alang da cost - he hed herd at dir wis still a settlement at Barentsburg aboot a hunder an fifty miles ta da nort."

The men found that launching the boats was no easy matter. On the side exposed to the gale the first boat to go down crashed against the ship's side, and was stove in before it could reach the water. The second, into which a number of the crew had climbed, actually reached the water, but was swamped by a huge wave almost as soon as it had cast off, the men in it all being thrown into the water and lost. On the lee side both boats were safely launched, and both managed to get away from the ship's side. Each boat managed to hoist a sail, but a small triangle was all the boats could carry because of the weather - a fierce blizzard with frightening seas.

When the brief daylight came up they could see, on their starboard side, the vague outline of land. The storm-force wind was abating, the sea was going down very noticeably, and while the daylight lasted the two boats kept each other in sight, and both increased the amount of sail they were using, at the same time edging gradually closer to the land. On the second night the boats became separated, and John's boat never saw the other again. Nothing was heard from the men on board that boat. The Captain, who had been on the second boat, had said that Barentsburg was probably 150 miles up the coast, and they knew that, at the speed they were sailing, they would need several days to cover that distance. They sailed on, but the men began to suffer badly.

"Efter aboot tree days," said John, "we wir raelly in a poor wye. Da wadder hed turned even caulder. Da sail froze laek a board. Wir claes wir aa weet fae da sea an da spray sweepin ower wis, an hit wis dat cauld at wir slips an wir drawers an wir socks aa froze ta wir boadies. Very shune nearly every wan o' wis wis sufferin fae frostbite, wir feet bein da warst. We hed naethin ta aet an we wir just aboot at da end o' wir tedder. We hed been sailin fairly closs in ta da cost, athoot ever seein onything at lookit laek a settlement, an da boys began ta dee, wan be wan. Ta begin wi, whin we pat a boady ower da side, somebody wid say twartree wirds ower him, but as time gude on, an we got waeker an waeker, hit wis a big effort just tae git da boady up on da gunnel an ower da side, an ony kind o' burial ceremony disappeared. We wid tip a man ower - a man wha hed mebbe been your pal on board da ship - athoot ony rael feelin o' sadness. I tink hit wis pairtly bekis we kent at ony wan o' wis cud be da nixt een, an at shunner or later we wid aa geen da sam wye. Dere wis harly a wird spokken ony mair - we hed nidder da interest nor da energy. Wan day we watched wan o' da boys tryin ta clooer up apo da gunnel. He tried an tried an finally managed it an dan just slipped inta da watter. Naebody tried ta stop him- naebody said a wird. Ah'm sure maist o' wis at dat moment felt laek döin da sam if we only hed da energy."

It was in this helpless state that the wind finally drove the boat over some rocks and onto a beach. Some of the men still had just enough strength to stand up and edge painfully up the shore from the sea. Before them stood several dilapidated huts, one of them, even to their almost uncaring eyes, looking in rather better condition than the others. It had a roof, a door and a window. When all who were able reached this hut and went inside John remembered vaguely counting them. They numbered eight. The most important thing which met their gaze was a small iron stove, and beside it a stack of wood. One man still had sufficient strength to get a fire going, thanks to his petrol lighter which had survived in working order despite submersion in sea-water. The heat of the fire thawed their clothes, and sufficient strength returned to enable some of them to go out again to try and help the rest of the men who had been in the boat. Seven of them lay where the sea had left them, frozen stiff. These fifteen were all who had survived the nightmare days and nights coming up along the Svalbard coast.

By the end of the first day ashore the number of survivors was down to six. They had no food, but there was no shortage of wood to keep the fire going, and they managed to dry out their clothes. They had found a pan in the hut which was still usable, and in it they melted snow, so they were not short of water. All of them had suffered from frostbite, mainly in the hands and feet, but the warmth and the water brought back a little life to their deprived bodies. Two of the boys, more able to move about than the others, discovered two tins of corned beef in one of the huts. It was like manna from heaven, but it didn't last. Two days later the same boys, on another foraging mission, discovered a bag with quite a lot of flour in it. Not able to carry it back in their weak state, they scrounged about until they found one or two tins, and carried them back full of flour.

Back in the hut they wondered how to make the best use of their find. As so often happened, they found themselves turning to John for advice. Frequently in the past they had found that the young Shetlander was endowed with a great deal of common sense - 'midder-wit' a Shetlander would have called it.

"I wisna shure whit da best answer wis," said John. "Dere's no dat muckle you kin dö wi floor on its ain. Bit I supposed we wid git some sort of brunnie if we mixed hit wi enoff watter ta mak a dough. We hed a fine muckle tin lid, an I shawed da boys hoo ta dö da mix, dan flatten oot da brunnie on ta da tin lid, an set him apo da tap o' da weel-stacked stove. Aa sax o' wis watched da bakin - we cud harly keep wir haands aff o' hit. Efter a bit we turned da brunnie ower, an gae da upper side a bit o' firin. Dan we tukk him aff, an divided him inta sax pieces. Boy, dat wis da best floorie bannock I ever tasted, even though hit hed nae saesonin - just floor an watter. As lang as da floor lested we keepit on makkin da brunnies. We aye aet dem just as dey cam aff da fire."

After about ten days in the hut one of the boys who was suffering badly with gangrene, died, so there were five. The flour ran out. Two of the remaining five were in a very bad way, unable to even stand up. They had no food at all now - just water. One of the boys still able to walk found a piece of what they concluded was frozen seal meat outside the hut, and this they thawed and chewed on tiny pieces of it. But within the next two days the two boys who were in the poorest condition both died, and they were down to three. One of them still had just enough strength to stand up, but even that was beyond John and the other lad.

"Dan cam da day," said John "whin we wir aa tree sittin on da floor wi wir backs up against da hut waa. Da fire i' da stove wis nearly oot, an we kent if hit did go oot we wid freeze whaur we sat. I wan doon on me haands an knees ta try an crawl ta da stove, bit I only wan half-wye afore I collapsed. Nane o' wis said a wird an I just lay dere. I tink aa tree o' wis at dat moment accepted at da end wisna far awa, an we cud dö naethin aboot hit. Efter a while some vague impulse fur survival shurly made me begin ta oag wance mair ower da floor. I wis on me knees, whin, suddenly, da hut door burst open, an a man in a kind o' white rigout stod lookin at wis. Dan anidder man in da sam kind o' rigoot appeared ahint him. Baith o' dem cam in an shut da door. Da first een lookit at me, on me knees on da floor, an said somethin laek "Hvem er doo?" I wis pretty sure dat soonded laek Norwegian, bit just said "Breetesh." Hit turned oot dat dey cud baith spaek English, an dey seemed specially interested whin I managed ta git oot, " Ah'm fae da Shetland Islands."

The Norwegians checked on the condition of the three men, and quickly realised just how desperate was their condition. They got the fire going at full blast again, then produced a little food which they were carrying with them as their own rations, and fed it slowly and carefully to the three survivors. When all three had perked up enough to understand what was being said to them, the Norwegians explained that they were out on a reconnaissance from a small Norwegian camp at Barentsburg. They were in touch with London by wireless, and had had a request to check whether there was any sign of boats having come ashore in the area south of Barentsburg. Clearly London was checking whether there had been any survivors from the *Highcliffe*. The Norwegians could see that the three men were far too weak to do anything to help themselves, so they explained that one of them would remain in the hut, while the other would ski back to base and bring a party with sledges to take the three to their camp. They would be back the following morning.

"You wid a tocht dat we wid a been ower da mun whin da Norskies appeared," said John. "Ta tell you da truth, I dunna tink we hed ony feelin aboot hit ava. I wid nivir hiv believed at you cood be dat far awa at you coodna cheer up whin you realised you hed been gien da gift o' life whin daeth hed seemed sae certain just a meenit earlier. Bit as da haet drink an da coarn o' maet began ta hae some effect, aa tree o' wis began ta feel da surge o' hop. As I said ta da boys - we're gaun ta see wir fokk again, efter aa. Fae dan on hit seemed a lang nicht waitin fur da Norwegians ta com an git wis. Bit noo, efter sae mony days an nichts o' despair, we hed some rael hop ta help wis pass da oors. Nane o' wis felt muckle laek sleepin."

The Norwegians returned next forenoon. They had three sledges, and the three British boys were carried out and laid carefully on the sledges, then covered up as warmly as possible against the freezing cold. All the Norwegians were on skis, and they covered the ground to their camp at Barentsburg, about nine miles away, in remarkably quick time, pulling the sledges behind them.
"I kin mind very little aboot dat trip," said John. "I tink I wisna mair dan half-conscious maest o' da time, bit I dö mind hit wis terrible cauld."

At the Norwegian camp they were well cared for. The huts were well heated, the bunks they were given comfortable enough. More inportantly, though there was no doctor in the camp, one of the Norwegians was the equivalent of a male nurse, and one thing he did know well was how to treat frostbite. None of the three lads had so far developed gangrene, and their sores were still treatable. There was no lack of food, and the Norwegians clearly realised that food was still the main thing the boys needed, but, realising how sensitive starved stomachs would be, they fed them sparingly to begin with. It was clear to be seen that all three had lost a great deal of weight. And gradually the amount of food was increased, as stomachs so long deprived began once again to deal with a normal intake.

For the first few days the boys hardly gave a thought to what lay ahead.
"As far as we wir concearned," said John, "aa at maittered wis dat we wir safe, warm an gittin as muckle maet as we cud haandle. I harly gae a tocht ta what wid com o' wis."

But gradually they began to absorb the situation. Although Svalbard had been evacutated earlier, the Norwegians had re-established a base camp, which was regularly in touch with London by wireless. The camp's chief value to the Allied cause was the daily provision of accurate weather reports, and now they could also report that they had in their camp three survivors from the *Highcliffe*. They added that all three were in vey poor condition, and recommended that families should not be informed until it became clear whether they were going to survive or not.

"I aksed dem if dey hed been able ta git wird ta London aboot wis," John recalled. "Dey said at dey hed done, an dey said as weel dat dey tocht at we wir dat poorly at hit wis mebbe better if wir fokk wirna telled just richt away, bekis dey wir far fae sure at we wir gaun ta makk hit." John fell silent for a moment, then he went on, "I said ta dem - Dere's nae wye Ah'm gaun ta conk oot noo. Just you keep comin wi mair o' yon guid maet o' yours an Ah'll surprise you."

Three more days passed and the boys had regained a degree of stength remarkably quickly. They had all been young and healthy when their troubles started, and now their robust constitutions stood them in good stead when they once more began to get proper treatment. Now their conversations were animated as they conjectured on how and when they might get away from Svalbard. It was at that very moment that the man in charge of the detachment came to them with a beaming smile.
"I have some good news for you. London has just told me that they hope to evacuate you very soon. They wouldn't say how, but I expect it will be a steamer on her way back to Britain from one of the convoys to Russia."
The boys' spitits rose immediately. Now they could actually look forward to landing in Britain once more. They had a sneaking feeling that the journey back might well have unpleasant surprises in store, but that was nothing new. "I tukk a while ta faa asleep dat nicht," said John.

Next morning John was just telling the Norwegians that now they were so much better and that there was hope of them getting back to Britain, their folks should be told that they were safe, and his friend was just saying that he would get a message to that effect sent that day, when they heard the drone of approaching aircraft engines. It was always assumed that the sound of aircraft engines meant the approach of German aircraft, and everyone went to the shelter which had been prepared. The single aircraft came on until it was directly overhead, then it went round in a half circle, losing height and finally settling on the smooth waters of the fjord. By that time it was plain for all to see that it had RAF markings, and one of the Norwegians said knowledgeably, "That is a Catalina flying boat." A rubber dinghy put off from the plane and some of the Norwegians went down to meet the men in it. They all returned to the camp, with the news that this was a plane which had come to take the survivors back to Britain.

"We wir telled ta git ready," John recalled. "Boy, dat didna takk lang. Dan we wir taen doon ta da peerie jetty an lifted inta da dinghy an paddled oot ta da plane. Dey bundled wis aboard, an richt away da plane started taxiing ower da watter. Suddenly we wir in da air an hit finally dawned on me at we wir on wir wye back ta Breetain. I cud hardly grasp hit, everything wis happenin sae fast."

The crew, all Norwegians, were very friendly, and all could speak some English. They were very solicitous about their guests' well-being, and they hadn't been airborne very long before they were handed mugs of steaming hot coffee. John was glad of it. Though they were bundled up in plenty of clothing, it was bitterly cold in the plane. Using his best English, he said to one of the crew.

"Is it always as cold as this in the plane?" "Well, it is colder when we're away north here inside the Arctic Circle, but we do suffer badly - particularly our feet. We wear several layers of clothing, but it's never enough." " How long will it take us to reach your base?" was John's next question. "Nearly twelve hours," he was told.

"Do you really have enough fuel for all that flying?" he asked.

"Oh, yes, just enough," he was told. "We knew that we were going on a long trip and we took a full load of fuel. We can stay in the air for 25/26 hours if there is need," was the cheerful reply.

"Are you allowed to tell us where we will be landing?" John asked.

"Sure, why not? But I do not think you will have heard of the place. It is very - how you say - remote and not very many people have ever heard of it. It is called Sullom Voe, and it is in the Shetland Islands, away to the north of Scotland. But it will not be difficult to get to your home from there, because steamers run from Lerwick to Aberdeen and Invergordon."

John looked at him in stunned silence, until finally the Norwegian, with concern in his voice, asked if he was all right.

"All right? I'm speechless! I belong to Shetland! You're taking me home - I live in lerwick, and I'm sure I'll easily get a lift down there. I can't believe it! An air taxi taking me from the North Pole to my door!"

The Norwegian couldn't fail to be affected by John's excitement, and soon the story had spread round all the crew - one of the Britishers was a Shetlander! His two friends were delighted as well - they just wished at that moment that they were Shetlanders too.

"We just fled on," said John. "I ken we wir a lang time in da air, bit da time passed athooot me harly noticin. Hit wis freezin cauld aa da time, bit I wis dat happy at I just ignored me feet an legs - dir wis nae feelin in dem. I coodna believe at I wid be seein you aa in just twartree oors Whin we landed at Sullom hit wis late, an dey tukk wis straight ta da Seeck Bay. Da M.O. cam alang richt away, an examined aa tree o' wis. I tink he tocht we wir tree poor lookin sowls, bit he just said we wid bide dere fur da nicht. By dat time hit wis efter midnicht, an ower late fur me ta set oot fur Lerrick, even if dey'd slippit me. In ony case I wanted ta be a bit brichter afore you saw me, or dan you wid'a tocht I wis at da last gasp.

As I lay i' da bed dat nicht I coodna help feelin foo lucky I wis. Oot o' a da seeventy men at hed made up da crew o' wir ship, dere wis only tree o' wis left, an I wis een o' dem. I kent I wis still in a poor wye, bit I wis very confident at I wid come ta be aa richt again. An dan, efter aa we'd been troo, ta hae an aeroplane takkin me richt back nearly ta me ain door! An Ah'd never been in a plane afore! Hit wis incredible! I said ta mesel, Nae wye, Jerry, is doo gaun ta be da end o' me in dis war. Ah'm gaun ta survive! Some o' da crew o' da Catalina hed followed wis up ta da Seeck Bay - we wir aa feelin as if we wir auld freends be dis time. Doo kens, Inga, yon Norskies ir rael fine fellows. An yon plane o' dirs - in da air fur mair dan a complete day if need be - yon's some plane! An noo ah'm hame, an Ah'm no gaun awa fur a peerie while onywye. I doot Ah'll hae ta pit on a stone or twa, at least, afore I geen."

John's audience had sat in rapt silence while his story unfolded. When he had finished, there was silence, and four pairs of eyes were fixed on him in a sort of amazed incredultiy. Three of his audience were silently wondering - how on earth has he survived all he's come through? Some of the story had gone over Ellen's head, but it was she who now broke the silence. Cuddling up to him she asserted, "Doo's hame noo, John, an doo's my big bridder. Doo haes ta takk me wi dee whin doo goes fur walks. Dere's ever sa mony things it I hae ta shaw dee."

Sheila had never let go of John's hand all the time he was talking, and Inga, who had listened with rapt attention, now went over to him and gave him a cuddle and a kiss.

"John, dis is da happiest day o' my life. I hed raelly gien up aa hoop o' ivir seeing dee again, an noo, here doo is, safe an weel. Whit tinks doo, Mom?" But Mom just sat smiling happily, the tears coursing down her cheeks.

"Dere's just wan thing, John, at Ah'm winderin aboot," said Inga. "Doo doesna ken, of coorse, bit da 'Times' cairried a story aboot a ship bein seen flottin upside doon in Arctic waters. Hit wis assumed at dat wis your ship?"

"Yea, I freyat ta tell you at efter we got awa fae da ship, five German bombers cam ower. Dey left wis alane, bit dey bombed da ship, an da force o' da explosions drave her aff o' da rocks, an shö just turned ower an da boddam cam up. Shö wis still flottin laek dat da last we saw o' her."

John stood up, looked fondly at his family and the girl who, it was now pretty clear, would be part of that family before long, and said,

"I ken dis is awful rude, bit will you aa forgie me if I geen ta bed. I doot Ah'm just no as strong as I tocht I wis - Ah'm just knackered. I promise dere'll be mair life in me da moarn."

After he had gone the four of them sat in companionable silence, the happiness that filled the room something that could almost be felt.

Chapter Thirteen

The Silver Lining

There was a spell after John came home when Inga was blissfully happy. She looked back over all the sadness of the past years - her father's death, the family's lack of money, granny's death, and then worst of all, the belief that John, too, had gone. But she put all that behind her, and subconsciously said to herself, "Dis is whit life sud be laek." To Mary she commented one night,

"Mary, doo kens aa da black cloods at's hung ower wis in da last twartree years?"

"Yea."

"Weel, I tink noo dat dey aa hed a silver lining!"

In the bank she was still the only girl member of staff, but she never thought about that now. She knew she did her work well, and she enjoyed doing it. Till the day the manager said to her,

"Inga, I want you to try something that no girl in this bank has ever done. I want you to go on the counter tomorrow." Seeing the look of dismay on her face, he continued hurriedly,

"It's just for one day, Inga. I'm convinced that sooner or later women will play a much bigger role in bank life than they do now, and I'm all for it. I want you to act as teller for a day, just to prove that a woman - and a very young one at that - can do the job. Now, you don't need to worry - I'll be keeping a close eye, and I'll be there if you get into difficulty."

So, next morning, after a thorough briefing, she took her place behind the counter. To the world she presented a calm, business-like exterior. Inside, she was pipperin. What customers could not see was that she was standing on a box. The bank had a fairly high counter, and Inga had never progressed upwards beyond five feet - hence the need for the box. Her first customer was a local businessman. Inga knew him by repute, which had him down as a somewhat hasty, intemperate character. He came in, looked at the regular teller who was busy with a customer, then looked at Inga. He hesitated, and she said, with a sweet smile, and perhaps just the hint of a tremor in her voice,
"Can I help you, sir?"
He came forward, and she could see that he wasn't sure how to handle the situation. A slip of a girl, dealing with his money! Before putting anything on the counter, he stated gruffly,
"Doo's brawly young for dis job, isna doo?" Inga gulped. She had rather expected this kind of question, and privately she wholly agreed with the customer. But she was sure the manager wasn't far away.
"Yes sir, I am young. But the manager has confidence that I can do the job. That's why I'm here. Do you wish to make a pay-in, sir?"
Still eyeing her dubiously, he tendered his poke of money and his pay-in book. She checked it all carefully, stamped his pay-in book in a professional manner, and handed it back to the customer.
"It is a pleasure handling your business, sir. We will always be pleased to serve you. Good morning, sir."

Still without speaking he left, turning at the door for a last backward glance. Inga gave vent to a huge sigh when he had gone. One down - how many more to come?

And so they went on, and her confidence grew as time passed. She could hardly believe the day was over when the big main doors were closed and locked, and her great adventure had ended. Everything checked out accurately, as she had been sure would be the case, and the manager congratulated her on an excellent day's work.

"I knew a woman could do it," he said. "And you did it - beautifully!"

It would be years before girls would become a common sight behind bank counters - indeed, it would be years before many girls were employed by banks, but every now and again, when the bank was short of staff through illness or for some other reason, Inga would find herself standing in for the regular teller, her faithful box raising her height. Though she was still as shy as ever, her experience in the bank was slowly but surely increasing her confidence in her own abilities, and, though she didn't know it, she was already displaying a maturity far beyond her years, as the bank manager had been quick to perceive.

At home John was slowly but steadily returning to fitness. The Sandness and Papa folk, when they heard of his dramatic return and poor physical condition, were quick to send mutton and tatties, with the exhortation to "Feed him weel!" Sheila was now a constant visitor to the house, her shyness gone, and Inga found that the two of them had much in common. The two Norwegians from the Catalina which had brought John home came back to see him whenever they had the opportunity. It took him a little while, but John began to realise that their visits had quickly become less concerned with checking on his well-being than on checking whether Inga and Mary were in the vicinity. Come to think of it, John mused, they really had seemed smitten the first time they met the girls!

John still had to make regular visits to his doctor, who refused to 'sign him off' till he was sure that he was fully fit again, so months passed and he was still at home. This time he didn't push the doctor to clear him. For one thing he realised that his recovery was very slow, and it was borne in on him that he had really been very near death's door. For another thing, he had now been involved in two sinkings, and you could push your luck just so far. So the months passed, and 1943 ended with him still at home.

By this time an invasion of Shetland by Germans from Norway was no longer feared, and gradually the Shetland garrison was run down, with the men involved being despatched to theatres of war where their presence was much more needed. The run-down of troops soon became evident in the town, and, of course, had an effect on the attendance at dances and other social occasions. But there was still a substantial Norwegian presence in the town from the MTBs and, occasionally, from a submarine. The boys from Sullom came in whenever they could, with the two who visited the Johnsons appearing probably more regularly than any of the others. It said a lot for the Shetlanders innate sense of security that there was no knowledge among Lerwick people of the activities of the Shetland Bus boats, first from Lunna and then from Scalloway. When one of the sub-chasers from Scalloway came into Lerwick on one occasion in 1944, she was the object of much speculation and rumour along the harbour front.

It became increasingly clear that the visits by the two young fellows from Sullom were first and foremost for the purpose of paying court to Inga and Mary. They were two fine-looking lads, and the girls had no difficulty at all in appreciating the attention the boys were giving them. It soon became the norm, when the two came to town, for the foursome to go to a dance, with John and Sheila occasionally accompanying them.

Inevitably, the girls discussed the situation.
"Yea," said Mary, "I laek Nils fine. He's very weel mainnered, an doo kens, Inga, he's awfil guid-lookin. An," with a smirk, "he haes smashin technique!"
Inga was never very forthcoming about her boy-friends.
"Yea, Hans is O.K. too."
"Is dat da best doo kin say aboot him?" Mary demanded. "Fae whit I kin see da twa o' you git on pritty weel."
"Yea, I ken, he's 'a bit of all right' I hiv ta say. Bit I dunna want ta git ower invloved just yit. Dey're awfil young, does doo no tink?"
"Young? Dey're baith aalder dan wis, Inga!"
"Yea, weel, I wisna meanin dir age sae muckle as dir midder-wit. Does doo no tink at dey're no very mature?"
Mary agreed with this to some extent, but she privately felt that Inga was being just a bit too choosy. As far as Inga was concerned, she hadn't yet realised that she would find boys of her own age to be immature. Her young life's experiences, added to an in-built maturity and intelligence beyond her years, meant that her actual age would always lag behind her mental attitudes.

But she did like Hans. He was a fine boy, and she was well aware that his feelings for her were very strong. While she didn't exactly keep him at arms' length, she was always in control of the situation between them, and, though any red-blooded young female Shetlander could be expected to enjoy a spot of snogging with an equally red-blooded young Norskie, things never got out of control. Still, it was nice to have a young man who was clearly gone on you, calling to take you to a dance or, maybe, to the pictures. He never seemed short of money, and he simply insisted on paying for everything - that, too, added to his attraction!

Though Hans and Nils could only get to town somewhat infrequently, Inga and Mary went to dances without them, and were never short of admirers. Occasionally someone would pay marked attention, and would progress as far as the top of Inga's steps, but such individuals seldom got any farther. At the back of her mind, Inga felt that Hans deserved to have the number one place in her attention. But she had to admit that she didn't know just where the situation was going to lead. The whole question was given voice one night when Mom said,
"Inga, is doo saerious aboot dis boy, Hans?"
"Mom, we're just good freends," Inga protested somewhat uneasily.
"Doo kens as weel as I dö at Hans tinks he's mair dan just a freend, Inga. Shuner or later doo'll hae ta makk dee mind up if freendship is aa hit's gaun ta be. Bekis, if hit's mair, doo kens he'll want dee ta geen ta Norwa wi' him. So, lass, tink whit doo's döin."

In a way Inga was glad her mother had put into words the thoughts which had been lurking in the back of her own mind. She raised the subject with Mary.
"Mary, is dee an Nils gittin saerious?" Mary looked at her.
"Whit wye does doo mean exactly, Inga?"
"Weel, is he ever spokken aboot you gittin mairried?"

"He's kind o' half mentioned hit, eence or twice. Bit whan he does I aye try ta shange da subject."

There was silence for a moment while both girls toyed with their thoughts.

"Weel, Mary, whit's doo gaun ta say if he does press fur an answer? Is doo ever tocht at doo cud geen ta Norwa wi him an settle doon dere?"

"Inga, Ah'm tocht aboot hit sometimes, an I do laek Nils an awfil lokk, bit I just dunna tink I cud geen an settle in Norwa. I kinna spaek a wird o' da language. Nils comes fae da island o' Bømlo, an dere's anidder fower boys i' da fainly. I dunna tink da prospects ir very good."

"So doo's gaun ta say 'No' if he aksis dee?"

"I tink sae. Whit aboot dee? Hans is fae Bømlo, isna he?"

"Yea, he is. Ah'm been worryin aboot dis a braw grain. Doo sees, mebbe da boys ir coontin on wis bein mair gone on dem dan we railly ir. Of coorse, I laek Nils, an I laek gaun ta dances wi him, an I dunna mind a bit o' cuddlin. Bit I hae nae tocht o' hit gaun ony farder. Ah'm faird we're no bein fair ta da boys. Mebbe dey're coontin on a lokk mair dan we're willin ta gie. Ah'm half tinkin I sood tell Hans whit da situation is."

Again there was silence. Finally Mary broke it.

"Da wye I see hit is - we're aa enjoyin wirsels. If da time comes at dey want ta press things a bit farder, dan we'll tell dem. Hoo aboot dat?"

Inga had reluctantly come to more or less the same conclusion, and there the girls let the matter rest. Let time take care of the problem. After all, there was a war on!

Chapter Fourteen

War Ends

Early in 1944 John was passed fit, and he went off once more to look for a ship. Soon they had got word that he had signed on again. This time, for some reason, Inga didn't worry so much. As John assured them, the U-boats were no longer the menace they had been. Ship losses had been dramatically reduced, and, as John said in a letter,

"I dunna wear me life-jacket twenty-four hoors a day noo." It seemed no time till the news of D-Day came, and, after it was clear that the Allied armies were not going to be driven back into the sea, the future suddenly took on a much rosier hue. Every one felt that the war couldn't last that much longer. The arrival of winter, and the Allies still not over the Rhine was a great disappointment, but the general feeling of optimism continued.

In Shetland the impact of war started to fade. Many of the Garrison troops had gone. The frequent visits of enemy aircraft had decreased to the odd single plane, and that was more often than not chased by a Spitfire from Sumburgh. Rationing remained as severe as ever - in fact, food had never been scarcer. Nor was there much in the way of clothes - even if there had been, no one had enough clothing coupons to buy very much. John came home for ten days in November, and now he could tell them that his ship had been involved in the Normandy landings.

"We gude in on D + 2," he said. "We cam in wi da flood, an drave her in as far as shö wid go. Yon boats at cud rin on da rodds as weel as sweem in da sea - 'ducks' dey caaed dem - cam alangside, an we lodded dem fae da cargo in da howlds. Dan, whin da ebb set in, wir ship wis left high an dry, an da trucks cam richt doon ta da saand, an up alangside, an we filled dem strecht oot o' da howlds. We didna laeve da ship much - we just gude up ower da saand an hed a look at whit we cud see fae da cost rodd. Dere wir mines aa alang da cost rodd bit da flail tanks hed exploded maist o' dem. Dere wir still a braw twartree bodies, maistly Canadian, I tink - lying unburied in a rig just in fae da rodd. I tink dey wir laekly in da middle o' a minefield an dat wis why dey wir still lyin. Whin da flood cam in again da ducks got busy wance mair, an we shun hed her empty. Dan sho flotted nae budder, an we just steamed awa among da wrecks an aa da idder bruck it wis washin back an fore."

Though John had seen nothing of the actual fighting, the odd German shell was still landing on the beach, and the whole thing had obviously left a deep impression on him. He was full of admiration for the boys who had landed on the first day.

"Hit most ha been an awfil experience weddin ashore among aa da booby traps an mines, under fire fae da Germans aa da time, an lodded doon wi heavy packs. I bet dey wir blyde ta win under da shelter o' da broo o' da beach fur a peerie while."
They had gone back to Normandy with a second load about a fortnight later.

"I cudna believe hit. Dey'd biggit an artifeecial herbor. Dey caad hit da Mulberry Harbour, an we simply tied up an da lorries cam doon alang da 'pier' an we unlodded inta dem. Hit wis in da shape o' a square, an da lorries cud drive richt roond hit. Dey'd hed a storm whin dey wir settin hit up an dat hed done a good bit o' damage, bit hit wis nearly aa repaired. Yon wis som job. I cudna git ower foo dey'd towed yon graet concrete caissons aa da wye fae England. An ootside hit dey'd sunk auld ships ta form a brakwatter. Boy, Ah've seen some sichts i' dis war!"

John assured them that the war would be over in a few months, and this time, when he went away, Inga hardly worried at all.

Sure enough, in May came VE Day. It was a marvellous day, and everyone celebrated. The following day was a sort of anti-climax - the war had finished and everything with which they had become familiar over the past six years would be changed. No more blackouts - streetlights on again - no more soldiers or sailors or airmen. And soon all the Shetland boys would be coming home. Peace was enough to make everyone happy, but there were more than a few misgivings about the future.

For Inga, perhaps the biggest source of her happiness was the knowledge that she didn't need to worry about John all the time any longer. And soon he would be home, they would be a family again, and they wouldn't need to keep lodgers. She was doing well in the bank, and had a rise in pay so that she was contributing in no small way to the family's upkeep. When she started at the bank her weekly pay had been £1.50, then it had gone up to £2, and now she was on £2.50, with real prospects of a further increase. But now there was a decision to be made which could not be postponed any longer. Nils and Hans were expecting to return to Norway any day now, and, as the girls had expected, both wanted the Shetland lasses to marry them and come to Norway. Inga's mind was now firmly made up - what she felt for Hans was not enough to take her to Norway, and, as nicely as possible she conveyed her decision to the young Norskie, while Mary was doing the same with her one. The young men accepted the girls' decisions with great disappointment but good grace, and all of them enjoyed the last dance together, with the boys expressing their thanks for all the good times they had had. For Inga a chapter in her life had closed, but her determination to learn the language remained.

When the MTBs left the harbour for the last time to return to Norway, the girls stood at the South Ness watching them pass. The crews were lined up on deck, waving to the crowds who had gathered along the shore to bid them farewell, for these little ships had become very dear to Lerwegians. Inga wondered just how many people had been like her and had counted them out when they went on a mission and anxiously counted them in again on their return. Now, in line ahead, they passed through the gap in the boom defence - open all the time now - and disappeared to the east for the last time. The girls had already said goodbye to the boys from Sullom, and now, as they turned silently homewards, both were in a pensive mood.

"Mary," said Inga, "I feel as if we've just reached da end o' a piece o' wir lives. Does doo hae dat feelin?"

"Ah'm just tinkin I micht ha been waitin noo ta try an fin some wye ta win ower ta Norwa ta join Nils an settle doon dere as his wife. Doo kens dir twartree Shetland lasses at's mairied Norwegians waitin ta geen ower. I did laek Nils, bit Ah'm blyde I didna agree ta mairry him. Hit'll laekly be a while afore I git mairried noo!"

"Ah'm blyde I said No da sam as dee," said Inga. Then with finality,

"Hans wis a fine boy, an I laekit him. Bit I didna raelly love him - I can admit dat noo. An I wid hae ta love a man afore I wid evir mairry him."

Chapter Fifteen

The Boys Return

There was no immediate demobilisation - the authorities, learning from the situation after the First War, didn't want a sudden supply of workers to glut the jobs' market. But some of the merchant navy boys, who were not bound by the same restraints, were fairly quickly home, and among them was John Johnson. For Inga, his return meant that life was back to normal. For John, it was time to take stock of his situation. He had his twenty-first birthday just after the war ended, and, though that meant he was still a young man, he had packed a life-time of hard experience into his late teenage years. He had been giving a lot of thought to his future, and somehow he just couldn't see himself sitting in a dreary office for the rest of his life. On board ship he had frequently found himself acting in the role of ship's carpenter, and it was work he really enjoyed, for he loved working with wood. His mind was soon made up - no more office work. He went to one of the local building firms, saw the boss, and explained the position to him. The result was better than he expected. He was taken on as an apprentice joiner, but, in view of his practical experience as a ship's carpenter, allied to his war service, he was put on a wage considerably higher than that of an apprentice. His mother was sorry to see him giving up a 'white collar job,' but Inga realised this was what he wanted, and was happy for him.

The bank had had two of the young men on its staff on active service, one in the navy and one in the army, and they both now returned within a week or two of each other. They were delighted to find a 'smashing young bit of stuff' on the staff, and Inga discovered that young ex-servicemen were quite a different kettle of fish from the older and staider men with whom she had become accustomed in the bank. Both of the young men had seen some pretty hard service involving considerable action, and their experiences had left their mark on them. Inga was conscious that the men who had been left at home regarded them warily, not quite sure what to make of them - for these were not the same two boys who had gone away early in 1940.

For their part the returned young men took some time to settle down to bank routine. They brought an irreverence to some of the procedures which were regarded as sacred cows, and incurred constant censorious glances from elderly staff members. There was a sort of careless brashness about them, and at times their comments could be extremely embarassing to a self-conscious girl.
"Lass, Inga, doo's a great improvement on auld Magnie. (Magnie was one of the elderly staff members.) Doo haes far better legs dan him - in fact, doo haes a smashin pair o' trams." Inga's response was muted - unless very red cheeks could be taken for a response. But she had to learn to live with it - and gradually their comments ceased to annoy. She knew there was no malice in anything they said. Both of them were single young men, and both obviously found Inga attractive. There were queries about her love life.

"Does doo hae a boyfriend, Inga?" Inga, by this time much more confident, returned,

"Dat's nane o' dy business, Willie." When Harry came with a similar question, he got the same response. Next came the direct approach.

"Dere's a dance in da Toon Hall da nicht. Is doo gaun, Inga?"

"I micht be."

"Will doo come wi' me?"

"No chance."

At the dance both boys sought dances, and at the end both proffered an escort home. Both were rebuffed. And so it went on, until both finally got the message. Inga liked them both, but that was as far as it went. Friends, yes, but nothing more.

When she and Mary went to Aberdeen for their first ever holiday, she derived considerable satisfaction from sending both boys an identical postcard. On the front was a picture of two tram-cars going up Union Street, and on the back was the simple statement, "Smashin trams, eh?"

While Inga loved her work, ahe also enjoyed the lighter moments of off-duty hours. Islesburgh House had begun to cater for various activities,among them a Girls' Choir, led by Jemima Peterson. Inga joined the Choir, which was soon participating in concerts not merely in the Garrison Theatre, but also in halls all over Shetland. These were still the days when country halls were far from being havens of comfort. Electricity still hadn't reached the country areas, so illumination was provided by means of Tilley and Colman pressurised paraffin lamps. Stages were usually pretty small, and curtains seldom failed to stick half-way when they were being either opened or closed. Sometimes there were no curtains at all. And, of course, sanitary arrangements were primitive in the extreme.

But these were the years immediately following the war, and the people of Shetland really appreciated any sort of entertainment after the arid trauma of the war years.

Always the Islesburgh concert played to packed halls, the audiences applauding every item with enthusuasm. Invariably a dance followed the concert, and it would be one o'clock at least before they climbed aboard the bus for the journey home. These were the days before the coming of Shetland's fine new roads, and the trip home from, say, North Roe took a considerable time. But these concerts were always on a Friday night so that most of the participants could look forward to a long lie in on Saturday morning.

Every Thursday night there was the church choir practice, for Inga continued to sing in the church choir every Sunday. There was a tremendous upsurge in dramatic activity at this time, and, apart from professional visits by Perth and Dundee Repertory Theatres, an annual Drama Festival was organised and it really blossomed. Competing teams came from all over Shetland to the Garrison. The Garrison was one legacy which the war had left to Shetland, and its large stage and excellent lighting proved ideal for this new wave of enthhusiam for drama. Islesburgh was of course involved in all this activity, and always provided one or more plays for the Festival. Inga got caught up in it, and found herself treading the boards as an actress. However, she quickly decided acting was not for her - her innate shyness prevented her from really enjoying an active part in drama. "Ah'll stick ta music," she decided.

The arrival of peace made little difference to the austere conditions in which everyone lived. But for young folk who had never been out of Shetland, with red blood surging through their veins, one of the first peace-time ambitions was 'a holiday sooth'. That cost money, and meant a considerable period of dedicated saving. It also meant having somewhere to stay at minimum cost when you arrived 'sooth'. Inga and Mary saved assiduously, and Inga finally reached the target which she had set herself - £25. Her production of knitted caps and gloves had provided a substantial part of the sum. The two of them boarded the *Magnus*, and bought 2nd class tickets. They were travelling 'steerage' - that was the cheapest way they could travel, and it left them a bit more money to spend. Though they didn't plan to go farther than Aberdeen, they found that there was plenty there that was new and exciting. There was now so much in the city to see - there were two theatres - there was the beach - umpteen picture houses - Hazelhead - Duthie Park - bus trips to various places in Aberdeenshire - a trip by train to Stonehaven. For the two young girls their first holiday 'sooth' was an enlightening experience, another step on the road to gaining confidence, and they couldn't wait for their next venture when, hopefully they could reach farther afield.

Inga had now turned twenty, and it dawned on her that some of her friends who were a similar age were getting married. In fact, she had already been bridesmaid for one of them. She was quietly aware that one or two of the weddings had been, of necessity, rushed affairs, but that was a situation she was determined to avoid. She supposed that, sooner or later, she, too, would get married. Likely she would have children - she felt she would like to be a mother. But so far she had met no one who had impressed her as possible husband material. Of course she was meeting plenty of young men. And, naturally, her life was not devoid of occasional brief liasons, which led to visits to the North Star as well as to dances, etc. In fact, one young man had progressed to the point where he took her home to meet his family. But always she extricated herself before any of the affairs reached danger point. From it all she learned that it was unlikely she would ever marry a boy her own age - it would have to be someone more mature.

So life went on very enjoyably. With John home and Ellen growing rapidly, they were once more a happy family, and money was not nearly such a problem as it used to be. Inga felt it would be just fine if things could continue like that. But then she had to face up to the fact that she had been seeing quite a lot of a certain young man over the last few weeks. He was an ex-serviceman who had been in the army, and was years older than her. Like her he was involved with Islesburgh House and inevitably they were frequently thrown together. He had been over six years in the army, had spent a year in Germany at war's end, and was slow to acclimatise to the ways of peace. He, too, was a member of the Islesburgh concert party, and soon it seemed a matter of course that they would sit together in the bus on the way back to town from country concerts and dances. From there visits to the North Star was a short step. He even had an old car that he had bought with money he had saved while in the army - it was all old cars at war's end, for no new cars were coming on the market at that time. He cheerfully admitted that the money from his car had been saved from his pay while living off the black market while stationed in Germany. Though a teacher, Inga found him very down to earth, and very intolerant of many long-standing customs which he found completely irrelevant and out-dated in the post-war world.

Almost without noticing, the situation developed to the point where they were spending quite a lot of time in the old car, and Inga's mother was becoming increasingly critical of the late hours Inga was keeping. The realisation was borne in on her that pretty soon she was likely to be faced with the need to make a decision. Her mother put it into words,

"Is doo saerious aboot yon fellow, Inga?"

"I dunna ken, Mom."

"He's far ower auld fur dee. He'll be fifty afore doo's forty. An he gude ta da Institute an da university. Doo widna feel at hom wi somebody laek dat. Does doo no tink doo sud brakk hit aff wi him afore hit geens ower far?"

"Ah'll see, Mom."

As she mused on what her mother had said, she realised that she did feel quite at home with him. Institute and university didn't seem to have had much effect on him, and his origins were little different from her own - born on a croft in the country instead of a room in a closs. But that very night, when they were sitting in the confortable darkness of the old car, with his arn around her, the day of reckoning arrived.

"Inga, is doo evir tocht whaur we're gaun? I tink hit's time I telled dee it I wid laek ta mairry dee. Whit does doo tink?"

Inga desperately played for time.

"Bertie, I dunna ken. Ah'm no hed time ta tink aboot hit."

"Whit's dere ta tink aboot? I love dee, an I want ta mairry dee. Dat's simple enoff, isna hit? Aa at I want ta ken is if doo loves me?"

"Bit - bit - dat's just da trouble, Bertie. Ah'm no sure."

"No sure? Does doo laek me?"

"Yea, I laek dee. I laek dee an awfil lokk. Can we no just laeve hit enoo? Kin we no geen on da wye we ir for a peerie while?"

Bertie realised that that was as far as he was going to get for the time being. At least she wasn't giving him the boot. He also realised that she was still very young - he was pushing her too much, maybe. There was plenty of time - he could wait. The fact that she hadn't sent him packing was cause for hope. His arm pulled her into a close embrace, to which she raised no objection, and when they kissed it was as enjoyable as ever. Of course there was plenty of time!

So they continued to go out together, and they were considered a couple by all their friends. Inga did quite a lot of soul-searching.

"I dö laek him a lokk," she told herself. "Bit dö I love him? Ah'm no sure if I raelly ken whit love is. If I agree ta mairry him kin I face livin wi him, day in, day oot?" Somewhat to her own surprise she discovered that, yes, she could face living with him. Yes, she could face wakening in the morning to find his face on the pillow next to her. As her mother had said, he was a lot older than her. But that maybe wasn't a bad thing. He didn't feel a lot older, and he had the maturity Inga always looked for, and his army experience had taught him how to make decisions whenever the need arose. He had a good sense of humour - she couldn't live with a man who couldn't see the funny side of life! - and, though she was pretty sure he loved her, he respected her as well. She realised suddenly that she had made her mind up - she did love him - she was going to marry him!

That night they were once agin sitting in the darkenss in the old car, each of them munching a pear. (A bag of pears was frequently Bertie's offering - there were few good chocolates about, and Inga loved pears!)

"Bertie, doo kens whit we wir spaekin aboot da idder nicht?"

Bertie was deliberately obtuse. " No, whit wis dat?"

"Doo minds! Doo wis spaekin aboot wis mebbe gettin mairried."

"Oh, yea, bit doo coodna makk de mind up. Doo didna ken whidder doo loved me or no. Foo does doo feel aboot hit noo?"

"Weel Ah'm still no fairly shör. Bit I tink mebbe I do. Ah'm been tinkin abbot hit, an I widna laek ta loss dee. So of doo still wants me, I tink mebbe we cud git mairried."

Bertie knew his girl better than she realised. He well knew how her mind worked. There would be no firm declaration of love until she was absolutely sure. That was fine by him, for he was absolutely sure he could make her happy, and he was confident that she would soon realise that she really did love him. What she was offering was more than enough. The pears forgotten, they sealed their pact in time-honoured fashion, and for both of them it was a night they would remember.

"Dis means at we're engaged, Inga. Ah'll hae ta git dee a ring. Doo kens I dunna hae muckle money, so hit'll no be a very expensive een. Will doo mind?"

"Of coorse no. Bit hit's only a fortnight till Christmas. Let's wait till dan ta tell everybody. Ah'll better warn dee Ah'm no sure whither Mom'll be plaised or no. Sho tinks doo's far ower auld!"

"Ah'm no very worried aboot Mom, if doo's no. Fae noo on hit's just dee an me."

So Inga and Bertie duly became engaged on Christmas Eve, and it was borne in on her that she had never been happier in her life. Teacher's pay was not very lavish in those days, neither was Inga's wage, so there wasn't very much money to play with. But they managed to overcome the biggest obstacle to married life by securing the tenancy of a small house in Quarff, and when they married in July, they blew what cash they had on a short honeymoon in Scotland. They came back to begin serious married life with Inga clear in her mind that marrying Bertie had been the right thing to do, and, yes, she did love him!

Chapter Sixteen

Matrimony

Inga had to admit to herself that being married was exciting. She was no longer Inga Johnson - she was Mrs Bertie Williamson! Now they had their own house, and, though it was small, it was all they required. Mistress of her own household - changed days from a room in a Closs! In one respect they had moved back - they had no running water and no electricity. A big tank caught the rainwater from the roof, and that served all their washing needs. A small well, with beautifully clear spring water, was only about a hundred yards from the house, and Inga made a daily trip to the well with her two pails. They had a Colman pressure lamp, but Bertie installed Calor Gas to light the sitting-room and the kitchen. The kitchen was equipped with a Raeburn heater/cooker. It kept the kitchen beautifully warm, it would burn peats or coal or wood, and Inga found that it was excellent for cooking purposes. To begin with Bertie came home for his dinner evey day, and she expended much effort and ingenuity in preparing tasty and interesting meals. But they began to realise that driving home for his midday meal was expensive petrol-wise, and so he began going to the school canteen. Although he paid much more than the children for a lunch, it was still more economical than going home.

When they got married, Inga automatically gave up her job in the bank. Those were the days when married women were not supposed to work - they would be keeping young, single women out of a job when they had a man to look after them. With only Bertie's wage coming in, they found the going pretty hard. It was lovely living out in the country, but it meant they had to run a car, and that was a heavy drain. They put off thinking about it, but what would happen when they finally had to replace it? For the time-being, at least. the newly-wed euphoria cocooned both of them and they refused to worry about anything. For Inga, it was bliss to settle down in the evenings on the sofa in the sitting-room before a scorching fire of mixed peats and coal in the grate, her man beside her, the wireless emitting a soothing background of music provided by Billy Cotton's band, while the gusts of a soouth-easterly gale snatched vainly at their stout little house. When they married they had discussed the question of a family. Bertie was very conscious of how hard Inga had to work all her young life, and he was anxious that, for a little while at least, she would be able to take things easy.

"Nae faimly fur a year, Inga," he had said, and she had gone along with that.

He added with a grin,

"I want dee ta hae a brakk - dat's da main raison. Bit I ken dere's a few auld biddies in da toon at ir shör we're hed ta git mairried. I just want ta see dir faces whin doo fails ta produce onything in twartree monts' time." Inga couldn't help recalling his words when, a few months later when she was in a shop one day, she overheard two elderly ladies exchanging choice items of current gossip. She almost burst out laughing when she heard one of them say,

"Doo kens peerie Inga Johnson at mairried yon young teacher at da Central? Is doo evir hard whither sho's hed her bairn yit?"

"Na, I saw her just da idder day. Dere's nae sign o' onything dere."

"Is doo shör? Everybody said at shö hed ta git mairried, an dere's nae smok athoot fire." But it appeared that peerie Inga was not about to give birth, and Inga thought she could detect a note of disappointment in the voices of the two gossip mongers.

She found that she had a lot of time on her hands. She kept the house spotless. She cooked. She knitted. She had never knitted so much, and the money she got for the knitting made a significant difference to their income. She came frequently to the town for the afternoons, but usually just sat with her mother - and knitted! She did some embroidery. She and Bertie went to the village hall whenever there was anything on - and sometimes they went across to the Gulberwick hall to play 500 - or watch a concert. But as the months went by she realised that her life, much as she enjoyed it, wasn't full enough to satisfy someone endowed with her restless energy.

Finally, in bed one night - their best discussions were always in bed - she began,

"Bertie, Ah'm turnin bored."

"Whit wye? I tocht doo wis happy." Her statement had left Bertie perturbed.

"Of coorse Ah'm happy. Bit I dunna hae enoch ta dö. Doo kens me Bertie - I need ta be busy."

"Weel, doo kinna git a job - doo kens dis thing dae hae here aboot mairried weemin if dir man is wirkin."

"Na, I ken - bit dere is wan thing at wid gie me somthin ta do."

"Whit's dat?"

"A bairn?"

Bertie was struck silent for a moment.

"Bit I tocht we wir gaun ta wait a bit afore a faimily?"

"I ken - bit, Bertie, dat wis dye idee. I just guid alang wi dat bekis I kent doo wis tinkin o' me. Bit I tink hit's been lang enoch noo. I wid laek ta hae a bairn."

Bertie raised himself on his elbow to look at her.

"My Goad, sae wid I. I wis just haddin aff bekis I tocht doo wid want a while o' freedom afore doo wis laandit wi an infant. Bit if doo raelly wants a bairn dan sae do I. I propose we do something aboot hit dis very nicht."

"I second dat proposal," said Inga. And then, solemnly, with a chuckle in her voice,

"Bit if hit doesna wirk richt away, we'll mebbe hae ta try some mair, Bertie. Tinks doo will doo be able fur dat?"

Anyway, they 'did something aboot hit,' and it wasn't very long before Inga could report that their efforts had been successful.

Over the next nine months there were times when Inga wondered what she'd let herself in for. There was morning sickness, there was the increasing feeling that she was becoming huge, and, considering how small she was to begin with, that was some feeling. There was, finally, the day when Bertie took her to the Maternity Annexe in Lovers' Loan. Though he left her with a cuddle and an encouraging smile, he was not a little worried. She was so small he feared she would have a hard time. It was the forenoon, and he returned home to sit by the phone. The new custom for fathers to be present at the birth had not yet come into force. But he was thankful that they were on their Easter holidays. The phone didn't ring, and he went back to the Annexe for the visiting hour. Nothing had happened except that Inga had already suffered considerably. That night he didn't go to bed, but the phone remained stubbornly silent. In the morning he went again to the annexe - things were no farther on and Inga was visibly weakening. She had had a really rough night and his heart went out to her. But he could be of no use to her. Home again to sit once more by the phone.

Finally it rang, and he had it off its rest before the first ring was finished. He heard the voice of Mr Lamont, Shetland's surgeon-consultant at the Gilbert Bain.

"That you, Bertie? I'm not going to let your wife lie up there any longer. We're taking her down here, and I'll do a Caesarean. Come into the GB at three o' clock." And he was away.

The minutes ticked away with maddening slowness, but on the dot of three he was at the Gilbert Bain, where he was shown into a small room and told to wait. It seemed an age, but it couldn't have been more than five minutes before a nurse came in carrying a small bundle in her arms. She proudly held out the bundle to Bertie with the smiling invitation,

"Meet your new daughter."

Any new-born infants he had ever seen had had red puckered faces, but when he looked at his daughter her face was as smooth as satin, and he thought he had never seen anything so beautiful. (Inga had to explain to him later that the smoothness was due to the Caesarean.) He had never believed infants bore any resemblance to anybody, but he realised at first glance just how much his daughter resembled her mother.

Mr Lamont and Dr Shand now appeared on the scene, Mr Lamont still in his theatre rig.

"Will she do?" he enquired. Bertie was still feeling very emotional, and got his words of thanks out with difficulty.

"How is Inga?" he asked.

"Och, she's fine. Come back at the visiting hour, and she'll be able to deal with you then. She's still recovering from the anaesthetic."

Bertie went out, got in the car and drove to the Hollanders' Knowe, where he drew off and parked. Sitting there he seasoned the relief - and the joy - which the last half-hour had brought him. He had had some narrow shaves in the army, and he had had some sad moments in his private life, but never had he gone through any experience which had stretched his emotions like this. The very thought that he could have lost Inga made him cringe. Not a praying man, he tried to give thanks for the happy outcome to the crisis just past. Keeping an eye on his watch, he was at the door of the Gilbert Bain again for the visiting hour. Inga was conscious, but he could see she was still very tired. He couldn't speak - he just cuddled her gently for a long time. Finally he whispered,
"Inga, I wis dat faerd I wis gaun ta loss dee." Weak as she was Inga well knew what he'd been through, for she knew what a worrier he was where she was concerned. Maybe she'd had the pain, but she had no doubt that he would willingly have changed places with her.
"Och, dunna be silly, Bertie. Dere wis nivir ony danger o' dat. Instead o' lossin me, doo's ended up wi twa o' wis. Is doo seen her? Whit tinks doo o' her? Wid doo redder a hed a boy?"
"Inga, shö's da boanniest thing I evir saw in my life. An shö's just da pikter o' dee. No, Ah'm no sorry at shö's a lass - Ah'm just dat happy at we hae wir bairn. Mind doo, whit Ah'm gaun ta do wi twa Ingas I dunna ken. Een o' dem wis mair dan enoch fur me!"

If they had been happy before, their happiness was doubled now. Little Sonja became the centre of their existence, and they watched her grow and develop with fascination and delight. Never had a bairn been as lovely as their Sonja. Never had there been a brighter infant than their Sonja. Their Sonja was just perfect. On the odd occasions when they went out in the evenings to visit friends, Sonja was well wrapped up, complete with mittens and bonnet, and placed in her carry cot. At their friends' house she would be deposited on their bed, where she slept unconcerned for the duration of the visit despite frequent incursions by everyone in the house 'just ta makk shör shö's aa richt.'

When she was nine months old she said her first word. Inga had been sure it would be 'Mom' or 'Dad'. But it wasn't - it was 'car'. It was definitely a word - and Sonja knew a car when she saw or heard one as she proved by the frequent repetition of the word on every suitable occasion. There were inoculations to be done, visits to the Clinic, and Inga saw many more bairns of a similar age to Sonja. As she admitted to Bertie one night, "Dere's a lokk o' yon idder bairns at look nearly as weel as wir Sonja, Bertie. I doot ta maist fokk Sonja wid be just laek da idder bairns. Bit sho'll aye be somethin special ta wis, willn shö?"

" Foo cud somebody at's da image o' wir Inga no be special?" demanded her husband gallantly.

So Sonja grew, quickly began to speak properly, and quickly began to walk. Gradually her parents came to terms with the fact that thye were just another proud young couple with their first bairn. When Sonja had been born - bit shö wisna raelly born, thought Inga, shö wis delivered - both doctors and nurses had laid strict warnings on both parents that there was to be no more bairns after the Caesarean for at least two years - preferably longer. For Bertie that meant - no more bairns. He

~ 118 ~

wasn't letting Inga go through it all again. No way. As he said to Inga,

"We're gotten wis a lovely bairn, an shö'll dö wis just fine. We're no takkin ony chances by haein anidder ane."

Inga said nothing. Bertie knew that when she said nothing in response to one of his statements that usually meant she disagreed, and he would hear all about it later.

When Sonja was two years old Inga reopened the subject.

"Bertie, hit's no richt at Sonja sud be an 'only' bairn. Dat's no good fur ony peerie ting."

Bertie had known he hadn't heard the last of this subject.

"Bit, Inga, doo minds whit da doctors said. Hit's no safe fur dee ta hae anidder bairn. Ah'm no gaun ta agree if dere's ony risk ta dee."

"Dey just said 'Not within two years.' Dey didna say I wis nivir ta hae anidder een."

"Weel, doo kanna hae anidder een athoot my help. An doo's no gittin dat help unless da doctor says hit's aricht."

So Inga went to see Dr Cadenhead, and came back to report that she had been cleared to have another child. Bertie didn't say much, but went to have a chat with Dr Cadenhead himself. He was reassured. Inga was perfectly healthy. She was small, and child-bearing might be harder for her than for some. But otherwise there was no reason for her not to have another child.

So Inga became pregnant again, and this time she was sure she was even bigger than she had been the first time. The months rolled slowly past, and as they approached term's end Bertie was like a cat on hot bricks. He became more and more anxious, and Inga had to read the riot act to him to calm him down. But there was no one more thankful than she when finally, at five o' clock one fine sunny morning, Bertie took her in to the old Annexe once again, having roused a kindly neighbour to baby-sit Sonja in his absence. He left Inga with consideraable trepidation, only half-hearing her lecture about not worrying and the need to make sure he looked after Sonja properly.

So once more it was a case of waiting for the phone to ring, but this time he discovered that Sonja needed so much attention that he hardly had time to worry. Sonja was very clear that she wanted the new baby to be a boy, and had exacted a promise from Dad that that's what would be arriving. What he would do if it was a girl he didn't know - Sonja would demand an answer. When the phone rang at twelve o' clock he picked it up almost absent-mindedly to be congratulated on the fact that his wife had just presented him with a nine-pound son. He sat down, took Inga on his knee, and started to tell her all about her new baby brother, etc., etc., and then suddenly realised that, in the sheer joy of the moment, he was simply babbling, and that his daughter was regarding him with some wonderment, mystified as to what was wrong with 'silly Daddy'. This time when he went in to visit Inga and see his son, she was looking well, and her only comment was typically Inga - "Ah'm blyde yon's ower." But her pride in her new son, and her desire to hear Bertie's praise of the new aquisition was clear to see. Once again Bertie's heart was filled with thankfulness for the happy outcome of their latest venture.

When the time came to bring mother and son home, Bertie took Sonja with him to the Annexe in the car. He had told her her little brother's name was Erik, and when he handed Inga and the baby into the car, Sonja peered into his face and repeated 'Erik - Erik' - then, looking at Inga, "My ain peerie bridder." At that moment Inga gave thanks that she had insisted on having a second bairn.

For the Williamnson family the days passed happily, with all the little ups and downs which are inevitable when there are children. Sonja seemed to come on by leaps and bounds, while it seemed no time at all till Erik was pedalling his little tricycle at breakneck speeds from room to room. There had been one anxious moment when he was little more than a year old when, in a fit of hilarity engendered by Sonja, he had managed to tip himself out of his high chair and on to the floor. There was a scramble by Inga and Bertie to check for broken bones, but Erik continued to giggle, trying to get Sonja to continue her antics. Falling out of his high chair was small beer in his busy world. Then came the pedal car. It cost £3, and to impecunious parents that was an extravagance. But the look on Erik's face when he got behind the wheel was worth a lot more than the price.

Suddenly Sonja was nearly five years old.
"Does doo realise Sonja'll hae ta start skule at Easter, Bertie?"
"Yea, Ah'm just been sittin here tinkin aboot dat."
"Every time we geen past da Quarff skule sho points at hit an declares, "Dat's my skule." I dunna tink we'll hae muckle budder gittin her ta geen on her first day."
"Yea, weel," Bertie started slowly, "I tink we sud mebbe spaek a bit mair aboot dat. I ken shö cudna be in better haands dan Daisy Thomson's, fur I ken shö's an excellent teacher, an a fine body furbye. Dere wid certainly be naethin wrang wi da education shö wid git at Quarff - in fact, hid wid be as guid as shö cud git onywye in Shetland. Bit Ah'm just been tinkin - dere's only ten bairns in da Quarff skule, wi nae mair dan twa in

ony age group. Whin Sonja starts, shö'll be da only bairn in her class. Is doo tocht aboot dat?"

"No, no raelly. Bit if shö's da only bairn in her class shö'll git very personal teachin, willn shö? Dat kinna be bad."

"Does doo mind whin doo wis persuadin me at we sud hae anidder bairn? Doo tocht hit wisna guid fur a bairn ta be an 'only child'."

Inga was silent, and he knew she'd made the connection.

"Whit doo's sayin is dat shö'll git guid teachin at Quarff, bit shö'll no be among bairns o' her ain age.."

"Yea, dat's whit Ah'm sayin, an I tink dat's a very important side o' education. In fact, I tink hit's dat important dat I wid laek ta enrol her at da Infant Skule in Lerrick, whaur shö'll be in a class o' mebbe forty bairns. Dere shö'll laern aboot livin wi idder fokk, an shö'll hae a shance ta see whidder shö's as guid as dem whin hit comes ta lessons. I cam fae a country skule at hed a lokk mair bairns dan Quarff, an I ken foo hard hit wis fur me ta fin me feet at da Institute."

Inga was very conscious of the weight of what Bertie was saying. She recalled her own infant class when she started school, and the wide variety of children with whom she lived, worked and played. She thought of Sonja at Quarff, the sole peerie lass in her class, with no one of comparable age to share in anything. Yes, what Bertie was saying was very true. She had just thought how handy it would be for Sonja to go to the Quarff school - she hadn't thought it through. And so it came about that they got permission to enrol Sonja at Lerwick Infant School, subject only to them providing the necessary transport. That was no problem, for Bertie was going in every day in any case, and she could stay at granny's after school until Dad came to pick her up.

So Sonja came and went every day with Dad. The only snag was that Dad, when leaving for home after school, frequently had a head still full of the day's problems, and thus preoccupied would arrive home to be met by an Inga whose first words were, "Whaur's Sonja?" Then it was back to town for a forgotten little girl. Not that she minded - she usually had a pal with her at granny's, and they played away quite happily. Sonja became quite accustomed to Dad forgetting her, but she knew that Mom would soon have him back to fetch her.

There were snags. Sonja's first winter at the Lerwick school turned out to be a winter of heavy snowfalls. Usually Bertie would leave the car at the main road overnight if there was the likliehood of snow, but it was heavy going to reach the car in the morning if the snow was deep, and it involved carrying Sonja piggy-back. For Inga this was not a happy state of affairs - and it was going to be worse when Erik started school as well. There was another conference in bed.

"Bertie, Ah'm no happy aboot Sonja gaun ta da toon whin dere's heavy snaw. Whit if you git straanded comin hom some nicht an hae ta bide in da car aa nicht? We kanna takk da risk o' dat."

"Ah'm been worryin aboot yon as weel. Mebbe we'll hae ta gie up takkin her ta toon an enrol her at Quarff efter aa."

"Well, mebbe. Dere is just wan idder possible answer. We cud try fur a hoose in da toon."

"A hoose in da toon? Doo's shurly no wantin ta geen an live in da toon? Life here in Quarff is far better dan hit'll evir be in da toon. Doo didna raelly mean yon, did doo?"

"Yea, Bertie, I did mean hit. Ah'm no wantin ta laeve Quarff. Ah'm been happier here dan Ah'm evir been afore. Of coorse, I dunna suppose we hae much shance o' a hoose, so whitevir we decide, hit'll laekly com ta naethin."

After they'd fully discussed the pros and cons, it was decided that Bertie would investigate the possibility of getting a house in the town. Sad as they would be to leave Quarff, a house in the town would simplify things for all of them, and would put Inga much closer to her mother, who was getting up in years. Bertie didn't want to leave Quarff, but clearly Inga felt that a move would be to the advantage of the baairns, and Bertie was well aware of how sensible and practical Inga was in her thinking. In the previous year Bertie had been given a strong hint by a member of the Education Committee that if he applied for a Junior High School headship vacancy his application would be very favourably received. As he pointed out to Inga it would mean considerably more money - and they could certainly do with that. He asked Inga what he was to do.

"Hit's no fur me ta say whit doo's ta do, Bertie. If doo tinks hit's whit doo wid laek, dan go ahead an apply. Ah'll go alang wi whitevir doo decides. Bit doo kens Ah'm very happy as we ir." Bertie didn't make an application - where Inga was concerned he could read between the lines.

But something else did happen. He came home one night and told Inga there was a good chance they might get an Education Committee house in the town; the present teacher had asked for a move, and the house would be vacant in a fortnight's time. He had been to the Education Offices, and he had been told that, subject to the Committee's approval, tenancy of the house would be allocated to the Williamson family from Quarff.

"So, Inga, we can say we've hed a rael bit o' luck dis time. Foo does doo feel - is doo blyde?"
Inga sat looking at him.

"I ken hit wis me at persuaded de ta dö dis. Bit I tink Ah'm gaun ta greet." And she proceeded to do just that. But three weeks later they went to town.

Chapter Seventeen

Family Life

The time the Williamsons spent in Quarff was probably the happiest part of Inga's life. She so much enjoyed being part of a small community where everyone knew everyone else, and they could count virtually everyone as their friend. She had thought they would stay there indefinitely, but when she felt that a move would be in the best interests of her bairns, then everything else had to take a back seat. And, having flit, she now had to adjust once more to life in the town.

The house they had been allocated was a typical Council house, purchased by the Education Committee and only a few years old. It had a nice bit of ground at the back for growing vegetables, and there was a sizeable back green where the bairns could play. There was plenty of house room - three bedrooms, a large living-room, a kitchen and a utility room, and, though sad at leaving Quarff, she was very pleased with her new house. Her mother had been given a move away from the old house in Commercial Road, and now lived just a few doors away from Inga, which enabled her to visit frequently and keep a watchful eye.

With Sonja at school, and Erik almost ready to go, Inga knew that soon she would once again have time on her hands. In the meantime she concentrated on her long-standing ambition - to learn Norwegian. A night-school class enabled her to sit and pass her O-Level exam, but there weren't all that many people about who could take her on to Higher exam level. Despite Norway's relatively close proximity, and the many links between them/us, not a school in Shetland offered Norwegian as a language. However, she reached the necessary level for a Higher, sat the exam and duly passed. Now all she needed was a trip to Noway to try out her new-found fluency on the natives. She wondered if they would understand her. Would she be able to hold conversations with them? In the meantime a borrowed Linguaphone course gave her practice in spare moments. The trip to Norway, she feared, lay far in the future.

The bairns had the ups and downs common to all bairns. Sonja distinguished herself by breaking an arm on two seperate occasions, while Erik set something of a record by having a plethora of childhood ailments all in the same year - measles, mumps, chicken-pox, German measles and, finally, scarlet fever. Scarlet fever at one time, not so far in the past, had been a deadly childhood ailment and had claimed many lives, but it had hardly been heard of in years. However, Bertie had had it when a boy, and had been in the Isolation hospital for eleven weeks, and he was immediately suspicious of Erik's symptoms. A hastily summoned doctor confirmed that it was, indeed, scarlet fever and, after administering an injection, went away to fetch a young colleague to view the first case of scarlet fever he had ever seen. He would probably never get to see another. Treatment proved quickly effective in Erik's case, and the worst was soon over. Where it came from was a mystery - and not another case was reported.

The school put on a concert in the Garrison Theatre, and among the many proud parents and members of the public in a packed hall were Sonja's Mom and Dad. When Sonja's class appeared to do a song and dance act, daughter Sonja was just one of a large group. But they were as proud of her as they would have been had she been doing a solo number, and Inga was delighted to notice that her daughter showed no signs of stage fright. Hopefully, she thought, she's not going to be as self-conscious as I was. She knew that she herself had gained a great deal of self-confidence since she became an 'old' married woman and mother. When she watched Bertie speaking at some gathering with complete assurance and aplomb, she drew encouragement from that, for he had told her that, when he was younger, he had been every bit as shy and retiring as she had been. He had simply forced himself, and now he could handle pretty well any situation.

The day arrived when Erik started school. Once more the house was empty, and once more Inga was bored. She spent more time with her mother, she knitted ceaselessly, she cleaned everything in the house that could clean - housework was not one of her favourite occupations - but she was still bored. Her heart leaped one day when the phone rang, and it was the bank manager at the other end of the phone. They had been keeping tabs on her, and they could tell her that the unwritten law that married women should not hold jobs was being followed more in the breach than the observance. They would very much like her to come back - even part-time - even for an hour or two a day. She promised she would have an answer for them the following morning.

When Bertie came home she told him about the phone call.

"Whit does doo tink, Bertie?" Bertie knew that she had been finding time hanging heavily on her hands, and he was pretty sure she was dead keen to get back to the bank.

"Weel, Inga, doo's da only een dat kens whidder doo can manage a faimly an rin a bank, at da sam time," said Bertie with a smile. "Bit I tink hit wid dö dee guid ta be back at wark. Hoo aboot doin just an hoor or twa a day ta begin wi, till doo sees hoo doo gits on?"

"Ah'm blyde dat's whit doo tinks. I wis plannin ta say at I wid come fae half-past nine till twal. Dat wid lat me git you lot aff ta da skule afore I geen oot, an Ah'll be haem again in time ta makk da denner."

"Noo, dat soonds ta me just aboot richt. Doo kens foo da bairns laek ta come haem fur da denners doo makks dem, so hit fits fine at doo kin wirk hit so doo's haem in time ta dö dat."

"Yea, I hear dee. Hit's fine fur aa tree bairns, fur da auldest een laeks his denners as muckle as da idder twa!"

So, with Bertie's blessing, Inga duly phoned the bank with her proposal. The manager was delighted, and off to work she went next day, happy and excited. Things worked out very well. On the rare occasion when one of the bairns was home ill, one of the neighbours whom they called 'Aunty Flo' was happy to come in and baby-sit for the two and a half hours that Inga was absent. As she said to Bertie,

"Hit's aa wirkin fine, bit I cudna takk on a full-time job. I hae ta be haandy if da bairns need me. Dey most ken at Ah'm here fur dem if da need arises. Ah'm spokken ta da heid teacher, an shö kens ta phone me at da bank if onything happens at dey need me."

She found that the bank had not lost its appeal. Some members of the old staff she had known so well were still there, and they seemed genuinely glad to see her back. She found that two other girls had been recruited to the staff, and it was pretty clear that, the way things were going, the female influence in bank staffing was on the increase. The two girls were both young newcomers, and clearly saw Inga as an older, much more mature woman. I shouldn't be surprised, she thought wryly, but I am still only thirty-three! I never thought I would feel ancient at that age! The nature of the work had changed considerably, and priorities had been amended. It wasn't long till she found herself taking stints at the counter again as a matter of course. The counter had undergone a welcome change, and was now low enough for her to be able to sit on a chair while dealing with the customers. Her box to stand on was no longer required. She found that counter duty no longer held any terrors for her - I must be getting more confidence, she thought. And now she found she knew a great many of the customers who appeared in front of her, and friendly greetings were the norm. That's one benefit of being ancient, she thought, you know so many more people!

She was surprised at how much the rate of pay had improved. Though she was only doing two and a half hours a day, she found that the amount she brought home weekly was by no means insignificant. Bertie's pay had also risen considerably over the years, and, for the first time in her life, Inga felt that she could now say to herself, "We're no ill aff." Though it was fine sometimes to buy something that they simply could not have afforded previously, what she appreciated most was the feeling of independence and security which the extra money brought.

They had continued to own a car, and one day Inga's growing self-confidence led her to announce,

"Bertie, I wid laek ta laern ta drive. Will doo teach me?"

Bertie had been more or less expecting this announcement for some time, because he had noted several occasions when Inga had said wistfully that she wished she could drive. But he thought it wise to introduce a note of caution.

"Yea, of coorse Ah'll teach dee. Bit doo kens, whin hit's a case o' da man teachin his wife ta drive, hit's weel kent dat mony a time hit leads ta trouble. I dunna ken why, bit dat's da wye hit is. Does doo ken, even da minister an his wife nearly cam ta blows whin he wis teachin her. Is doo shör doo wants ta risk hit?"

Inga was sure, and for the first lesson they went to Scatsta, where the freedom of the old tarmacadamed runway proved ideal for early lessons. Inga was not mechanically minded, so the intricacies of a modern car were a pretty mysterious bag of tricks. But they graduated to the open road, where sheer determination ensured slow but steady progress was made, to the point where it was decided that Inga would sit her driving test. On the dreaded morning Bertie left Inga, tester and car, and, conscious that his normally composed wife was a mass of nerves, waited in some trepidation for the completion of the test. No surprise there - Inga had failed.

So it was back to the drawing board. An intitial phase of "Ah'll nevir laern ta pass" was followed by a renewal of the fighting spirit, and a return to the wheel. Bertie was conscious that lessons were a little more strained now, and he had almost decided to ask her to take instruction with a professional teacher when the day came that she was practising hill starts at Dale. Never had she been more determined to get it right, but somehow things weren't going quite as well as she would have wished. It was unintentional, but maybe Bertie had allowed a note of criticism to creep into his voice. His small wife, outrage in every one of her sixty inches, opened the door, stepped out, came round to the passenger side and, in icy tones, informed him,

"Dat's enoff. Doo kin drive hame. Dere'll be nae mair lessons - Ah'll nevir laern ta drive wi dee teachin me."

So they duly returned home in a frigid silence which continued until bedtime when, happily, a thaw set in. From now on Bertie arranged for Inga to have lessons from Andrew Leslie and Andrew Gifford, and, in due course, she resat her test - and passed! Never once did she remind Bertie of his shortcomings as an instructor, and, once she started driving on her own, she quickly gained confidence. But whatever it was that cars had under their bonnets remained a dark secret, and on the one occasion when she needed to change a wheel, she opened the boot and then stood looking helpless until a Good Samaritan came past, saw the damsel in distress and came to the rescue. The helpless look had done it again!

There had been few holidays since they married, but it came to Inga one day that there was little point trying to save every spare penny if they couldn't get some enjoyment out of it. So a conference with Bertie produced the decision to take the bairns 'sooth' this summer to let them see just what the outside world was like. As Bertie recalled,

"The first time I gude steerage on the *Magnus* ta Aiberdeen, an dan da train doon ta Edinburgh. Man, I felt an eediot finnin me wye fae da boat ta da station, dan gittin a ticket fur da train - hit wis aa completely new an unkent ta me. Dan whin we cam ta Edinburgh da Waverley seemed laek a graet underground cave. Hit widda been aesy ta takk a taxi ta da address at I hed, bit I didna hae da money fur dat. So I followed da crood up da steps an cam oot in Princes Street - I kent dat's whaur hit wis fae da pikters I'd seen. Tramcars wir passin aa da time, bit I didna ken whit een ta git on. Finally I aksed a kindly lookin auld man whit tram I sudd takk ta git ta East Preston Street, an he telled me ta geen roond da coarner an git on a number seeven - hit wid takk me up da Bridges. Dan I wis ta aks da conductor ta pitt me aff at da street I wanted. I cud a done wi somebody wi me ta hadd me haand, so I want wir bairns ta ken dir wye aroond whin dey finally geen oot inta da muckle world."

Inga was in complete agreement, and in due course they boarded the *St Clair* at Victoria Pier, and travelled in a 4-berth cabin - a first class, of course. It was all new to the bairns - and a first class- cabin was new to Inga as well. In Aberdeen Bertie had booked them into the Douglas Hotel, and this, too, was new to the bairns. In Inga's case the only time she had stayed in a hotel had been on her honeymoon. There was a slight hiatus when Erik refused to travel in the hotel lift, but insisted on using the stairs. The first day was spent in Union Street, looking at the shops, and down at the Pleasure Beach, where the amusements were like an Aladdin's cave to the children. Bedtime that day saw two pretty tired young people seeking sleep in their 'own' room. In the morning, when Inga went through to see them, she found Erik missing. A still sleepy Sonja could tell her that he was helping one of the maids, and there she found him, riding up and down in the lift with a young maid who had clearly come under his spell. This was the boy who had an aversion to lifts no farther back than yesterday!

They had planned only a week's holiday, for two reasons. One was that Inga felt that a week for the four of them would cost as much as they should spend, and, secondly, she didn't want them to get fed up by staying too long. They went for a bus tour as far as Balmoral, and they went by train as far as Dundee, and visited friends there. They made many trips on the trams, until the bairns had complete confidence in boarding them and getting off. Hazelhead and Duthie Park were favourite haunts, and a visit to the theatre to see a variety show was a highlight. Though football was out of season, they went to Pittodrie to see a youth match, for Erik was already keen on football.

They had breakfast every morning in the big dining-room, and on one or two nights they had dinner as well. The table settings and the waiter service were new experiences for the young ones, but thanks to Inga's instructions, and their own quick appreciation of what was right and what was wrong, they were soon behaving like old hands. One morning in the dining-room a bus party of French tourists arrived for breakfast. The visitors were a source of absolute fascination for Sonja and Erik. Most of them could produce only the most fractured version of English, all of which was uttered in loud voices. This had the bairns in a state of non-stop giggles. The waitresses were addressed as 'Mees', and Mees was kept on the hop with their requests. "Mees, more choice, plees," was a constantly repeated order, at which Sonja finally surrendered to outright laughter. She had quickly cottoned on to the fact that the French wanted more orange juice, but poor Mees was at a loss and the French were becoming more and more demanding. Inga had great difficulty in restraining Sonja from entering the fray to explain to the waitress what the strangers wanted.

So the Williamson family seemed to be set fair for the voyage of life. Inga had more than once broached the subject of, "Mebbe we sood tink aboot haein anidder bairn, Bertie?" It was not something she considered she should insist on, but had Bertie shown any sign of wanting an increased family she would have immediately agreed. But Bertie's attitude was clearly negative. "We can be tankfoo at we hae twa lovely bairns, an doo's nane da waar. Bit we're no takkin ony mair shances. I love me bairns - bit I love me wife tö, an I dunna want ta rin da risk o' lossin her." For once Inga felt that Bertie could enjoy the feeling that he had laid down the law. It was never put into words but she knew - and Bertie knew - that when Inga really made her mind up about something, then- that was that!

As she lay in bed one night she found her mind casting back to the days in the Closs, when they all lived in one room. Strangely, she never saw these days as being in any way days of hardship.
"We hed naethin, bit we managed, an we wir happy enoch in wir ain wye. Bit Ah'm blyde wir bairns dunna hae ta geen troo aa at I gude troo."
From there it was a short trip to consider the next possible advance in their lives. She knew they couldn't afford it yet, but the way things were going they might sooner or later be able to build their own house. "Bertie will takk some persuadin," she thought drowsily. "He'll nivir tink we kin afford hit. Bit," - and her face wore a smile as sleep claimed her - "he usually comes ta agree wi me whin he tinks I raelly want somethin. An widna hit be fine if we cood big wir hoose in een o'da lanes?"

Postscript

Inga Mary Henderson lay sound asleep in her crib. She had just celebrated her first birthday, and she was exhausted, because it had been a really busy day. She had done a lot of walking, and that had been tiring, because she was still learning to walk properly. She had also laughed a lot, and had become very impatient sometimes when the grown-ups didn't seem to understand what she was telling them. But all in all it had been a smashing day, and now she slept the sleep of happy exhaustion.

Her mother and father, their arms around each other, stood looking proudly down at the sleeping child.
"Isna shö boannie, Jim?" mother Emma asked.
"Shö's lovely, Emma," father Jim replied. "Nearly as lovely as doo is."

Emma Leask had married Jim Henderson a year and a half ago, in March of 1996. They were still as much in love as they had been on the day they were married. It was strange, in a way, how it had all come about.

The two families - the Leasks and the Hendersons - had lived within half a mile of each other, and Emma was just a month younger than Jim. They had gone through primary in the same class, and had been good enough friends, for Emma was one of the few girls Jim perceived as being almost as good as a boy. She even played football with the boys. Then it was on to the Anderson High, and again they shared many of the same classes. Emma continued to be a good pal, and she was happy to have Jim for a friend. They both completed their secondary education with four 'As' in their Highers, and both were accepted by Edinburgh University, Jim going into digs away up the Bridges, Emma into a Hall off Dalkeith Road.

And there it might all have stalled, had not Jim gone into the Union one night when there was a dance on. Almost the first person he saw on the floor was Emma, and the student she was dancing with seemed to be doing quite a line with her, and he could see no sign of her discouraging him. He found himself staring at them, and realised that he resented the possessive way the unknown student was holding Emma. It came to him like a bolt from the blue that this was not Emma, his pal, as good as any boy. Where had his eyes been this last year or two? This was a lovely young woman - beautiful of face and lissom of figure. As he sipped his glass of beer his eyes never left the couple, and he suddenly found that he was violently jealous of the young man.

When the dance ended Emma's friend did not leave her. Clearly, thought Jim, he must be well in. But as the music restarted, and before the two could again take the floor, he nipped quickly over, took her hand, and, with a casual "My dance, I think," led her away without a backward glance. Emma hadn't seen him coming, but now he could swear she had reacted with pleasure when she turned and saw him. Soon they were on the floor, and he had her in his arms. He had danced with her before, but he had never seen her as anything more than 'one of the boys'. Now he was acutely conscious of how she went out and in at all the right places - in short he had a lovely bundle of femininity in his arms. The music changed to a smoochy waltz, and he held her closer. This was really something - how could he have been such a mug up to now? Impulsively he bent and kissed her - he could swear she responded willingly. Emma had been a little surprised to see Jim, because they had had little contact for a while. She knew fine well that he saw her as just another boy, and while she would have been glad if he could have seen her as something more attractive, she was prepared to settle for anything as long as it continued their friendship. But he was different tonight. He was holding her differently. Then, when he kissed her, and she responded - maintaining a degree of restraint with difficulty - she'd waited a long time for him to make this move! - she thought delightedly that at long last he'd found out that she was a girl!

After another dance or two - the ignored rival had now disappeared - they left the Union, and started to wander homewards, their arms round each other. Both of them were vividly aware that things had changed - they had entered willingly and eagerly on a completely new relationship. Here and there, in the darker spaces between the streetlamps, they would stop and kiss and cuddle, but this was no ordinary snog - this was like an electric current running between them. After a lengthy session outside her Hall, he left, with a firm date for the following evening.

The affair went from strength to strength. He had a landlady who encouraged him to bring his young lady along, and Emma smuggled him into her room in the Hall from time to time, so they managed to find space to express their feelings for each other. But they were both practical young people.

"Emma, dis is daft. Why do we no look fur a peerie flat so at we kin live tagidder? Doo's sure doo loves me, isna doo?"

"Yea, Ah'm in nae doot aboot dat." And she took time off to demonstrate this to his satisfaction. "Bit whit will dye fokk - an my fokk - tink whin dey hear at we're livin tagidder?"

"I dunna care whit dey tink. We're inta da nineties o' da twentieth century - an dere's an awful lokk o' couples livin tagidder an no mairried."

So they went ahead and found a small flat down in the New Town - in Queen Street - and quickly moved in their meagre belongings. Then they told their parents. Emma's mother seemed to accept the situation with equanimity. Jim's mother Sonja discussed it with husband Alan. As she had expected, he took it in his stride.

"Good luck ta dem," he said. "We ken whit a fine lass Emma is. I wiss I'd hed da sense at dir age ta dö whit dey're doin."

Whit will gran say, tinks doo?" Perhaps Alan knew gran Inga better than Sonja thought, for his only comment was, "I dunna tink shö'll be very worried."

And he was right. Inga just said,

"Weel, hit's dir lives. Dey're baith sensible enoch, and auld enoch, ta ken whit dey're doin." But she somehow forgot to mention the new situation to Bertie.

As far as the two young students were concerned, they were blissfully happy with their new life-style. With some of the money he made from his summer holiday job, Jim bought Emma an engagement ring, which she wore with pride. "We'll git mairried as shun as I kin git a job efter we graduate," Jim stated with authority. Meanwhile they lived, learned, loved and lusted with great gusto. And they found it cost them less than if they had been living separately.

They came back to Shetland after they graduated. Jim had been offered a job at the Fisheries' College, and Emma had been taken on as secretary by one of the fish-processing companies. She was certainly qualified for something better, but it kept them together, and, as they had planned, they got married. The parents from both sides, of course, were at the wedding, and so were the grandparents. It was a very happy occasion, and Jim marvelled at how lightly gran Inga could still trip the light fantastic, and with such obvious enjoyment. Grandad Bertie still seemed reasonably fresh, but his legs clearly didn't carry him as lightly as they once had done, and he sat out most of the dances. However, he never seemed short of someone to talk to. Jim would probably have been interested to hear his grandparents chat after they were in bed that night.

"Bertie, hit seems a lang time fae we wir mairried, bit I still mind wir weddin as clearly as if hit wis yisterday. Tinks doo ir we baith gaun ta makk hit ta wir golden weddin?"

The way Bertie had been feeling lately made him rather doubt that, but he responded confidently that of course they would.

"Shö's a fine lass, Emma. Ah'm blyde at Jim tok her. I dunna tink we need hae ony worries aboot dem," said Inga.

"Na, shö'll keep Jim in oarder da sam wye at doo's keepit me. Naebody lookin at dee wid evir imagine just whit a poowerful wumman doo is. Doo tinks Ah'm nevir noticed, bit Ah'm aye kent wha wears da breeks in dis hoose! Ah'm no complainin - Ah'm enjoyed every meenit o' it. Ah'm sure Jim'll be just laek me - a poor saft sowl!"

Then, as on every night for over forty years, he brought the conversation to a close by kissing his peerie, powerful wife, then turned over and went to sleep.

For a few years after they married, Inga and Bertie had gone to Inga's mother every year for their Christmas dinner. Then, as she got older, Inga took over the duty, and now for many years the whole family had come to Inga's for their Christmas feed. To begin with, it had been to the house they had been allocated by the Education Committee. But Inga had never given up her dream of one day owning their own home. Once Sonja and Erik were old enough, she had started working full-time at the Bank. Bertie had been promoted, and their incomes had risen. She knew that Bertie still did not feel that owning their own house was a viable possibility, but Inga never gave up hope.

Then came the day when an advert appeared in the 'Shetland Times'. The Town Council had a piece of land which they were dividing into four house sites, all of which would be sold to four people wishing to build their own houses. Inga read and re-read the advert. That evening she casually pointed it out to Bertie.
"Dere'll be evir sae mony efter yon - we dunna hae a hop. In ony case we kinna afford hit."
For the moment she said no more. She had noted the closing date for applications. She waited. Three nights before the closing date she reopened the discussion.
"Doo says we widna hae a hop o' gittin wan o' yon sites. Bit dere wid be nae haerm in pittin in an application - just fur fun."
"Inga, da shances ir at yon sites ir already earmarked fur someen. Doo kens whit Cooncils ir laek."
"Go on, Bertie - pit in an application - just ta plaese me." And she shamelessly went across to give him a kiss and a cuddle. As usual Bertie succumbed and wrote the application, promptly forgetting all about it.

It was on an evening three or four weeks later that a friend of theirs came to call. He had an announcement to make.

"Ah'm just been spaekin ta Tammy Nicolson - doo kens, Bertie, he's on da Cooncil - an he hed a bit o' good news fur me. At dir Cooncil meetin da nicht dey considered da allocation o' yon fower hoose sites, an he telled me at I wis gotten een o' dem."

Inga's heart sank, but she warmly congratulated their friend on his good fortune. Bertie recalled that they, too, had put in an application, but he had known they didn't have a chance. "Hit wis just ta plaese Inga, doo kens."

The friend had worn a smile like a Cheshire cat ever since he had come to the door.

"I wisna feenished tellin you me news, fur Tammy telled me da names o' aa da fower folk at hed gotten sites. An, Bertie, wan o' dem wis you - you're gotten een da sam as me."

When they were finally convinced that they were not having their legs pulled, their friend departed, and Inga and Bertie were left looking at each other in silence. Inga waited for Bertie to speak - she knew what it would be.

"Inga, doo kens hit's nae use ta wis. Ah'm ower auld ta takk on a mortgage, an we dunna hae enoch money o' wir ain ta big a hoose. We'll just hae ta write in an say at we're shanged wir minds."

Inga had lived with her man too long to make the mistake of pressing him too hard. They went to bed. Her lack of argument didn't fool Bertie. The matter wasn't closed. There would be more.

And there was. The subject was reopened next evening. Inga wnated to know how much a house would cost. Then she wanted Bertie to reckon up in detail just how much money they could put up themselves. Then she reminded him that he'd had an account with the bank since the thirties, and he'd never once had an overdraft. She wanted him to go to the bank and ask if the bank would be prepared to loan them enough to complete the house once they'd used up all their own money.

"Bertie, doo kens I wirk in da bank, an dey're kent me fur a while noo. An dey ken at doo's been a good customer fur therty years or mair. We're makkin a good wage atween wis, an I tink da bank wid look on wis as a gude risk. Please, Bertie, go an spaek wi da manager." So Bertie duly went and spoke to the manager. To his surprise his request received immediate sympathetic consideration. Their financial state was quickly checked, and the manager said forthrightly that he had known Inga and Bertie a long time - and he reckoned the bank had a duty to help people like them. Bertie was told to go ahead. A sufficient overdraft would be made available to meet their needs.

Inga was waiting impatiently to hear Bertie's report, and was over the moon when he told her.

"Bit, hit'll mean rinnin wirsels inta debt wi da Bank, Inga. Whit if I wis ta dee afore we kin git hit paid aff, an doo wis left on dee ain?"

Inga was not to be put off. He wasn't going to die - she wouldn't let him! They would pay off the overdraft together. She would never forgive him if they didn't take this wonderful chance that they had been given. So, as Bertie had known they would, they went ahead and built their house. With Erik's help they finished the inside walls of the upper floor under their own steam, and they did all the papering and painting themselves. Papering ceilings was not a job which appealed strongly to Bertie, and the language at times became strongly flavoured. Inga was always on hand to help and try to ensure there was not a complete blow-up. And when it was all finished, she was proud of it, and loved to sit looking down on the familiar harbour with all its comings and goings. Once again she was living in the lanes, but not in the way she had done as a child, and to Bertie's happy surprise the overdraft was paid off inside two years.

Every year she looked forward to Christmas Day, for then the whole family gathered toagether. Sonja insisted on making a contribution to the festive meal, usually in the form of a starter. But Inga was always up early, starting her preparations. The turkey was the first thought - it had to be big, and it needed to be in the oven early to give it enough time to cook. Bertie was usually pressed into service peeling potatoes, and at a pinch he could always be persuaded to set the table. But Inga tried to curb his activities these days because he was less able than in days gone by. By one o' clock all was well under control, and Inga went to trig herself up before the gang's arrival. Bertie was ordered to put on the lovely cardigan Sonja had knitted for him, and then they both sat down to 'solist fur twartree meenits', Bertie with his customary pre-prandial glass of whisky, Inga with an orange juice. In days gone by she had sampled various forms of alcohol, but had never found one she enjoyed, so confined herself to soft drinks, no matter the occasion. Bertie fully approved - he reckoned it was a lot cheaper! As he said - they couldn't both afford to drink! Erik had never married, and now he joined them for a few quiet minutes before the influx. Although Inga would have been glad to see him married, she was privately relieved that he still lived with them, for there was so much that Bertie wasn't able to do now - after all, he'd turned eighty, and it was a godsend to have Erik and his willing hands still with them. The three of them sat chatting quietly and happily until a rumble at the door and a cheerful shout announced the arrival of Sonja and Coy.

Today Sonja had a stranger with them whom she introduced as Astrid, a friend over from Norway to savour and experience a Shetland Christmas. She had heard that Inga spoke Norwegian, and soon the two of them were chattering away like old friends as Astrid helped Inga with the preparations. Who will Sonja have with her next year, Inga wondered. Last year it had been Oleg, a Russian whom she'd met in Moscow when she was over there as part of her university course. Before that had been Martine, an American girl from Chicago, and before that a French girl from Lyons, who had become a doctor. Never a dull moment with Sonja around!

The next arrival was John. Nowadays he lived with his wife in Edinburgh, but this year had come north on his own, a rare Christmas visit just to see Inga. He had been out visiting friends, and had just returned when Jim and Emma arrived, accompanied by a wide-awake Miss Inga Mary Henderson, who immediately became the centre of attention. The carry-cot was in attendance, because the parents were hopeful that all the attention and excitement would bring about the need for sleep before the afternoon was out. From this point on, a close observer would have been able to note that Inga had unobstrusively delegated dinner duties to the three girls, for clearly there was no one who could hold the baby Inga on their knee as competently as Inga. Had anyone suggested that she was proud that her name had been passed on, she would have pooh-pooed the very idea, but secretly she was as proud as Punch. Inga Mary was the apple of her eye.

Last to arrive was Olav, Sonja's younger son. He had with him his girlfriend Fiona, a pretty girl whom he'd been escorting now for nearly a year, and to all appearances the young pair were very attached to each other. Today they had Alex with them, a friend of Olav's up from Edinburgh. Inga approved of Fiona, but occasionally wished that she would wear skirts and frocks at least a little longer. Bertie thought Fiona had lovely legs, and was all in favour of the short skirts. Inga had expressed her views to Bertie previously.

"Bertie, lasses sood always laeve somethin ta da imagination. Whit wid doo a tocht o'me if I'd cled mesel laek yon whin we wir coortin?"

"I tink hit wid'a been fine, an I ken da boys in da bank wid'a loved dat. Doo minds dey tocht doo hed a smashin pair o' trams!" and Bertie beat a hasty retreat. The only family member missing today was Ellen, but she was married now with her own family, and the scene in her own house would be very similar to that in the Williamsons'.

Eventually everyone was seated at the table. Bertie had unearthed and cleaned up the bairns' old high-chair, and Inga Mary was proudly ensconced on high where she could see all that was going on. This was a smashing day - clearly everyone thought her the most important person there! Sonja's starter was consumed, then it was on to the main business of the afternoon - the turkey - and this year Erik did the carving. Noise somewhat abated while the serious business of eating was carried out, and then came the annual treat - Inga's pavlova and bløt-cake. Every year by popular request Inga produced these sweets. As children Sonja and Erik had loved them, and then Jim and Olav had followed suit. This year Inga Mary was introduced to the two dishes. Judging by the contented gurgles as mouth, face and chair all received dollops of the sweets she could now be counted among the enthusiasts.

The dinner consumed and the table cleared, everyone sat around in replete contentment. Inga Mary had succumbed, and now lay sound asleep in the carry-cot. As the conversation ebbed and flowed, Inga sat momentarily outside herself lookin at her family, listening with half an ear to the conversation. To think that she and Bertie were by now almost within sight of their golden wedding. And what a happy half a century it had been. They had both come from virtually nothing, and now here they were, in their own house, still in the lanes, but leading a life so far removed from her beginnings. For much of the time they had scraped to make ends meet, but hard work and careful housekeeping had brought them to their present state of independence.

A week or two earlier when they had received their Christmas bonus from the Charitable Trust, Inga had looked at the cheque, then said to Bertie,
"I winder if we're twa o' da fat cats at yon Cooncillor is on aboot?"
"If we ir, I dunna tink doo's needin ta slim just bekis o' him. We're baith wrocht hard fur ony coarn o' fat at we hae. Mebbe yon man'll see things differently whin he's auld enoch ta git da bonus himsel."

For Inga Christmas Day was the happiest day of the year, for then she had around her all those who were nearest and dearest. Inevitably she drifted into the bedroom where her namesake lay, and stood gazing down at the small face which at that moment lighted up with a smile at some fancy which had entered her mind in her sleep. Inga couldn't help thinking of the cradle which ahd stood by the side of the bed in their single room in Chapel House, and which had played such an important role in the lives of all three Johnson children. It was still painful to recall the days after her father died - the grief, the tears, the blackness, the poverty. What a struggle her mother had had to bring them up - what sacrifices she had made. It had not been easy - but they had won through, and so much happiness had followed.

"Na, we'll nevir be fat cats," she mused, "bit we're no ill aff, an dat's aa at onybody needs. An as fur dee, peerie mite," and she stroked the golden hair of her first great grandchild, "may doo nevir want fur onything - but may doo nevir hae ower muckle."